CW00835700

SWISS BANK ACCOUNTS AND INVESTMENT MANAGEMENT

Your Own Completely-Legal, Super-Safe, Tax-Free Offshore Account -- And Not Even The IRS Has To Know

Compiled and edited by
David Falkayn for
SwissInvesting.com

Books for Business
New York - Hong Kong

Swiss Bank Accounts and Investment Management: Your Own Completely-Legal, Super-Safe, Tax-Free Off-shore Account -- And not Even the IRS Has to Know

Compiled and edited by
David Falkayn for
SwissInvesting.com

ISBN: 0-89499-203-1

Books for Business
New York - Hong Kong
http://www.BusinessBooksInternational.com

Contents

Foreword

This book is written for the serious person of means who wants safety and performance from invested wealth.

No matter where you live or what economic and political hazards your country of residence presents to investment you owe it to yourself to consider Switzerland as the place to put your hard-earned money, especially in the Swiss insurance annuity. In my experience a comparison of the Swiss annuity with more traditional forms of asset protection shows that an annuity can serve the same function as trusts or similar legal devices but produces a far greater return for your money with complete safety and less complexity.

Among the few who do not care about money and asset protection, ignorance about Switzerland perhaps can be forgiven. Some people do tend to equate we Swiss with chocolate, cheese, fine watches and skiing in the Alps. Even such sophisticates as Graham Green and Orson Wells in their 1949 screenplay "The Third Man," set in post-World War II Vienna, had Wells sneer: "In Switzerland they had brotherly love, five hundred years of democracy and peace and what did they produce? The cuckoo clock!" Since Wells was playing the role of an international entrepreneur his character certainly should have had a greater appreciation of the Swiss than this flippant remark reflects.

Here we are concerned with personal wealth, its creation, expansion and preservation. In that context it is not understatement to describe the Swiss financial system's unequalled world record as unique in combining investor safety with assured earnings. Thoughtful people who value financial freedom and asset protection know this well. The question is why any serious foreign investor fails to avail himself of the many benefits of the Swiss system. The answer is; the serious investor never fails!

There are many reasons for people, particularly citizens of the United States, to seek asset protection.

Few seem to realize that the laws of the United States grant more favorable legal rights to plaintiffs (including creditors) than any other jurisdiction in the world. Persons of wealth are prime targets for litigation which can end in loss of assets and destruction of their way of life. *The Wall Street Journal* reported on May 7, 1991 that "nearly 100 million new cases were added to the dockets of the nation's state court system in 1989" and that figure did not take into account federal court cases.

Every person should plan for the important aspects of their financial life. One major area is estate planning which hopefully will insure that at the time of death property passes without incident according to the deceased's wishes. The second area is lifetime financial planning which seeks to build and manage an investable estate to provide assets and income. The third area, the one I will address, is asset protection, an indispensable element without which the other two can be rendered meaningless.

My suggestion is that the Swiss annuity and the portfolio bond are the best and least complicated of all current asset protection devices.

In these pages I will first set the scene for discussion of the Swiss insurance annuity by telling you about the history of my country, our people and the national character. I do so because I want you to feel at home with us, so much so that you will know your trust and investments can be placed in Switzerland with absolute confidence. And in learning about my homeland I believe you will share my view that in all the world our unique country is the matchless haven for your safe investments.

Swiss History Provides The Base For Asset Protection

The Swiss Confederation originated more than 700 years ago on August 1, 1291, shortly after the death of the Hapsburg ruler, Rudolf I. The forest-dwelling chieftains of Uri, Schwyz and Unterwalden who lived within his domain met secretly in a meadow at the foot of St. Gothard's Pass. Fear of a less benevolent ruler than Rudolf, whose castle was nearby, produced a mutual defense league which eventually would expand into 26 highly independent "cantons," as we Swiss call our states. In 1315 the league's warriors so decisively repulsed foreign invaders at Lake Lucerne that the Swiss reputation for fierce combat was established throughout Europe. Years later, in 1829 revolutionary Paris, the overture to Rossini's opera based on Schiller's play, William Tell, told the world about a genuine hero of these 14th century Swiss battles. Some of our fighting ancestors hired out as mercenaries, the last vestiges of which are today's Vatican Papal Swiss Guards.

In 1515, after defeat by the French in Lombardy, the Swiss officially proclaimed perpetual neutrality: "We will attack no one, participate in no war, will make no alliance, and will defend ourselves." In 1648, under the Treaty of Westphalia, the Swiss league became independent of the Holy Roman Empire and in 1798, the people then known as Helvetians, formed the Helvetic Republic under temporary French influence, soon rejected. In 1803 Napoleon Bonaparte, in the Act of Mediation, gratuitously gave the Republic a short-lived constitution. In the aftermath of Waterloo in 1815 we Swiss quickly reverted to our decentralized cantonal system. Most importantly for our subsequent history, in that same year at the Congress of Vienna the Federated Powers of Austria, France, Great Britain, Portugal, Spain, Sweden, Prussia and Russia guaranteed the inviolability of Swiss territory and our perpetual neutrality. In 1919 the Treaty of Versailles ending the First World War also gave international recognition to Swiss neutrality.

For 250 years, as European empires and nations have emerged and disappeared, in war and in peace, we have followed the example set by our ancestors, defending our territory and maintaining strict neutrality among all nations.

It is most important for you as an investor to understand the deeply ingrained attitude this historic Swiss neutrality has imparted to our people. In the more than 700 years of our nationhood we have at times had to fight to protect our land but Switzerland has never been an aggressor nor allied with an aggressor nation. In two world wars in this century our borders were fully defended but without any international or military alliances. After the Second World War the Swiss people, aware of our history, overwhelmingly rejected in plebiscite proposed membership in the United Nations but our nation willingly has served as the international headquarters for numerous U.N. and other activities including the U.S.-Soviet disarmament negotiations and the International Red Cross. Similarly, in a 1992 national plebiscite Swiss voters rejected membership in the European Community (EC), one fear being that at some future date the EC bureaucrats might attempt to interfere with Swiss privacy and banking laws. After the plebiscite, significantly increased amounts of European cash flowed into Swiss banks, confirming the perception this is the safe place to protect assets.

Swiss neutrality is more than military in character; it also means economic neutrality. This has had a significant impact on our financial system by instilling in our citizens an abiding respect for the creation, preservation and privacy of individual wealth. There have never been Swiss exchange controls imposed on capital outflows and in my opinion there never will be. Unlike almost every other nation Switzerland has never held hostage capital deposited within its borders either by its own citizens or foreigners. Simply by avoiding international conflicts and never taking sides Switzerland has become a world-recognized refuge for capital from every nation.

Today 6.8 million Swiss live in the Swiss Confederation, a republic of twenty-two cantons, covering 15,943 square miles (41,293 sq. km), an area half the size of the U.S. State of Maine; a mountainous nation bounded on the west and northwest by France, the north by Germany, the east by Austria and the south by Italy. By comparison, Switzerland would fit into the State of Texas seventeen times over.

Remarkably diverse for so small a nation, we Swiss reflect our neighbors' historic and cultural influences, speaking four official languages, French (18%), German dialects (65%), Italian (10%) and Romansh (4%), a linguistic descendant of the original Latin spoken by the Romans who controlled the area 2,000 years ago. It is not unusual for two Swiss from different areas to converse in a mutual third language, often English. Despite this diversity we enjoy a stable and unified society with a strong national identity and pride.

Economic Stability

Alone basic Swiss statistics might conjure up the picture of a third world country; more than a quarter of all land barren and uninhabitable, without mineral resources such as gold, oil or coal; a population density twice that of China and seven times that of the United States; a land highly dependent on imported raw materials. But we have more than compensated for these short comings in other ways as you shall see.

By contrast, we are statistically the richest people in the world with the highest per capita income ($27,750 annually; compared to second place Japan at $23,319) and have one of the lowest rates of unemployment (0.5% in 1993). National economic growth over the last four years has averaged 2.8% and inflation remains historically low. Second only to Germany, 35% of our people work in manufacturing. In spite of the impression created by bucolic tourism posters, agriculture employs only 5% and the great majority, 60%, works in the service sector, led by tourism for which Switzerland is justly world famous.

One of the established characteristics the world rightly associates with Swiss products is high-quality and precision. Depending almost completely on imported raw materials, and with a comparatively small domestic market, Swiss products must compete in the international market place and that requires excellent quality. As a result we have become leaders in the development of advanced technology in industries such as machinery, optics, watches, clocks, precision scientific and other instruments, chemicals, pharmaceuticals and metal products.

A concomitant aspect of our productivity is the realization by both management and labor that their best interests lie in cooperation. Since 1973 when the metal industry workers were the first to renounce officially the strike as a bargaining tool many other worker groups have followed suit. In turn, Swiss business opens its books to workers and keeps them informed of their progress and plans. As a consequence, strikes of any kind are almost unheard of and there has been no industrial strike in 50 years. Workers are well paid and it is common for Swiss management to give a "13th month's salary" as a bonus at the end of each year.

Our national attitude towards work owes much to the so-called "Protestant work ethic" developed by Swiss theologian John Calvin who founded his church in Geneva in the 16th century. His teachings included hard work and thrift, hallmarks of our people and the banking system to this day. We Swiss have the highest levels of personal savings compared to gross domestic product (GDP) of any nation of the world: $15,000 per person. We also work a longer work week than any in Europe: an average of 42.5 hours compared to 37 hours in Europe as a whole. Not only is unemployment low (0.7% average during the 1980's), the nation has the lowest crime and poverty rates of any nation.

Education and the Mind

Situated as it is geographically, Switzerland has been an intellectual international crossroads for European thought for many centuries. In addition to Calvin, Swiss-born John Jacque Rosseau was one of the inspirations of the American Revolution, exporting his writings on Swiss-style democracy to the rest of Europe and the New World. From Voltaire to Lenin lack of Swiss censorship codes have allowed publication of a huge variety of opinions by exiles from other nations who have taken refuge in Switzerland. Nearly a million foreign nationals live here, of whom 750,000 are part of the labor force with temporary residence permits.

The Federal Institute of Technology in Zurich (founded in 1855) has produced more Nobel Prize recipients than any other scientific school in the world. There are seven universities, the oldest in Basle, founded in 1460, modeled on the German style, governed by a rector and a senate, divided into faculties of law, medicine, theology, economics, science and the humanities.

Secondary education, which has been compulsory since 1874, is financed, administered and controlled by the cantons and communes within their borders. This makes for variety but usually nine years education is a minimum requirement. The Swiss education system is geared to preparing students to enter the market place and earn a living. Thus the 350,000 secondary students from 12 to 15 years old attend gymnasia and other schools specializing in commerce, business administration, trades, technical, art, domestic economy (or "home economics" as the Americans say), various aspects of agriculture and dairy management among others. There are about 400,000 students in primary grades and another 150,000 in nursery schools.

Of course I am prejudiced about my home land but I believe it accurate to describe our people as hard working, disciplined, meticulous, certainly conservative, but friendly in a reserved way. It has been said, I believe correctly, that we Swiss combine the best of the Germanic love of order with the Latin freedom of spirit and appreciation of quality and craftsmanship.

The World's One True Democracy

Independence of spirit and stability of character is certainly reflected in our decentralized system of government. Perhaps more than anywhere in the world we Swiss truly are a people who directly govern ourselves.

Under our Constitution adopted in 1874 the highest authority is vested in the electorate, all citizens over twenty years old. Here the rights of the individual are paramount.

In 26 cantons and over 3,000 municipalities or communes political power is exercised by the people who directly control the formal governing bodies. In some cantons such as Zurich, all laws, agreements with other cantons, and major financial matters must be submitted to popular vote. In other areas such as Appenzell, Glarus and Unterwalden the people exercise their powers directly in the Landgemeinde, periodic open air assemblies of all citizens of full age. Most citizens identify politically and culturally with their canton, from the beginning the powerful and highly independent components of the Confederation whose first formal constitution was not adopted until 1848.

Nationally, all amendments to the Swiss Constitution must be submitted to voters before they become effective. Perhaps most importantly, as a continuing safeguard, upon petition of 50,000 voters, less than 1% of the electorate, (or by request of eight cantons) any law or international treaty must be subject to a referendum for voter approval. Using the constitutional power of the popular initiative 100,000 voters can propose a constitutional amendment and bring it to a national vote.

To give you some idea of our collective national political judgment here is how we voted in national referenda in recent years:

- Against "soak the rich" taxes on high wage earners.
- Against a national uniform tax rate for all cantons which would have forced low tax areas to raise taxes.
- Against allowing the federal government to operate at a deficit.
- Against "temporary authority" for federal deficits or tax increases during times of low economic growth.
- Against reduction of the work week from 44 to 40 hours.
- Against increasing annual paid vacations from 3 to 4 weeks.
- Against reduction of the age to receive federal old age pensions.
- Against giving workers authority over management in operating businesses.

This innate national conservatism has important implications for foreign investors as well. The voters are always likely to reject any law which gives the government greater control over private finances. For example on May 20, 1984 a majority of the voters voted down by a margin of three to one a Socialist Party initiative proposing a serious weakening of Swiss banking secrecy laws. Federal politicians know they can and will be called to account by the voters and this acts as a constant restraint against proposals lacking a broad consensus among the people.

Structure of Government

The federal government is supreme in national matters such as foreign affairs, treaties, defense, transport, communications, issuance of money and banking, and certain multi-cantonal public works such as highways and railways. All other unenumerated powers are retained by the people and exercised by them through the cantons or communes.

National legislative authority is vested in a parliament or Federal Assembly of two chambers, a Standerat, or Council of States, composed of two members from each of the 26 cantons and a popularly-elected 200 member Nationalrat, or National Council whose members serve four year terms and are apportioned on a cantonal population basis. The Assembly meets four times annually for a few weeks and elects the seven-member Federal Council, the national executive body.

The members of the Federal Council, who act as heads of administrative departments, annually rotate the presidency of the Swiss Confederation, a quaint constitutional device which results in the average citizen rarely knowing (or caring) who the nation's president may be at any given time.

For most purposes the people are sovereign and exercise their powers through the elected cantonal governments including parliaments which vary in size and organization. The cantons retain all the powers not delegated to the federal government which gives them considerable control. On the local level the 3,000 communes, some with as few as 50 citizens, decide issues such as public works or perhaps the selection of teachers or a judge.

As you see the Swiss political system is one of extensive checks and balances with the national government subject to referendum as well as the retained powers of the cantons. An even greater check is our inherent moderation and conservatism, especially when dealing with economic, social, or financial matters.

A Word About National Defense

For those unfamiliar with Switzerland there may be an initial tendency to think neutrality equates with weakness.

Such an impression is absolutely wrong.

From the beginning our neutrality has been an armed neutrality. We maintain one of the largest citizen armies, the national militia, in all Europe with 625,000 men, almost 10% of our population obligated for continuing periodic military service between the ages of 20 and 50. We have long had fortifications at all the entrances to the Alps and on the important passes crossing the Alps and the Jura mountains. Large scale destructive capacity is in place to destroy 3,000 bridges and tunnels should an invasion occur. Civil defense has been taken seriously ever since the very real threat posed by the advent of the World War in the 1930's. There is now a nationwide system of nuclear fallout shelters sufficient for the entire population, complete with full hospitals and a year's provisions of water and food in event of any catastrophe in war or peace.

Every Swiss soldier undergoes an initial training of 118 days and thereafter 20 days annually are given over to refresher training and maneuvers. Full salary or wages are paid by employers during this service. In the event of an emergency, an additional 400,000 reserves in the Civil National Defense Service can be called up immediately. The Swiss Air Force has nearly 300 fighters as well as surface to air missiles and other modern weapons and can call up 45,000 men upon mobilization. And yet we spend only 1.9% of our gross domestic product on defense, the rest being volunteer effort.

With an extraordinary degree of mutual civic trust each soldier keeps and maintains in readiness his automatic weapon and other equipment at home and must engage in shooting practice to keep up proficiency. It is estimated there are more than 600,000 assault weapons in Swiss homes with thousands of rounds of ammunition for each gun. Although decentralized, the existence of our national militia has been a constant warning to any potential invader. Even Hitler's generals were able to convince him in 1939 to avoid an attack on Switzerland as not worth the effort or the real possibility of defeat.

The army, which is partially under the control of the cantons, has no general except in time of war when the Federal Assembly appoints one. Since the fall of Napoleon Bonaparte at Waterloo in 1815 such an appointment has been unnecessary.

For us in Switzerland, defense is a cooperative community effort without the unnecessary distinctions between civilians and military which exist elsewhere in the world. We value our our freedom and should it become necessary we will fight for it.

An Oasis of Financial Security

Writing of his travels in Switzerland, the American expatriate Henry James commented on the Swiss "national genius for frugality." He may have had in mind the observation by the Dutch humanist Desiderius Erasmus: "Frugality makes a handsome income."

Based on the principle of economic frugality, our Swiss banking and financial system has been successfully operating essentially in its present form for nearly three hundred years. Swiss bankers served the nations of Europe as long ago as the Middle Ages. Whatever the cause, from the time of the French Revolution to the advent of Nazi Germany to this day, foreign citizens entrust their wealth to us because they know Switzerland is a safe financial refuge.

One major difference which sets Switzerland apart from financial markets elsewhere is our established international outlook. This attitude is the product of generations of experience banking across national borders, first with our important neighbors of France, Germany, Italy and Austria (until 1918 the seat of the Hapsburg's Austro-Hungarian Empire) and now as bankers to the world. For centuries Swiss banks have maintained banking accounts in all the nations of Europe and in the United States for more than a hundred years. After London and New York, Switzerland is one of the world's three top financial centers with banks holding over US$400 billion in assets. Since World

War II Switzerland has also become the undisputed leading financial "haven" for capital in search of protection. For people with money to protect, whether a little or a lot, Switzerland offers the world's safest repository.

I have already touched upon some of the factors which make Switzerland so attractive for foreign investment including political and social stability, safe financial institutions and a conservative national character noted for thrift, a strong work ethic and respect for private property.

Let us now consider another major source of confidence for foreign investors looking to Switzerland.

World's Most Stable Currency

Unlike most national currencies the Swiss franc is more than just a bit of paper backed by a government's promise. Swiss law requires that all francs in circulation must be backed by a minimum of 40% gold reserve. Actual gold reserves amount to at least 56% backing because the value used is the old Swiss Central Bank price of US$42.22/oz. This means that at today's world gold market price Swiss gold reserves amount to many times the face value of all issued Swiss francs.

Over the long term the Swiss franc has steadily increased in value against all other currencies making it the world's best investment currency today. Undoubtedly our national political and economic stability has contributed to the value of the franc's superior level of performance. Other currencies, the Deutchmark and the Japanese yen for example, temporarily rose, spurred by spurts of economic growth or speculation, but these rising stars soon slipped with the exposure of underlying economic weakness such as the high price of German political reunification or the growing dimensions of the Japanese paper debt crisis.

The notorious weakness of the American dollar of course reflects continuing grave economic problems in the United States including a huge national debt, ballooning consumer and corporate debt, unfunded private and government debt and pension liabilities and the savings and loan bailout and the potential banking crisis.

Even with what may seem to many as low interest rates, historically the Swiss franc has provided a total long term (1970-1990) return of more than 10% measured in U.S. dollars. When the exchange rate is also considered, the yield is even greater. (By comparison the highest 1993 interest rate paid by an American insurance company, Kansas City Life, on its life annuities was 7.5% declining to 6.5% after five years). Since 1926, when the franc became completely independent, it has increased its value against all other major currencies with few brief execeptions.

An investor who purchased 10,000 Swiss francs in the mid-1980's for the then rate of US$3,875 in less than three years would have doubled the value to US$7,800 and by 1990 would have increased to over US$8,000 not counting interest.

Keep in mind the enduring anti-inflation value of the solid Swiss franc, an important factor when you consider investing in a Swiss insurance annuity. Currency choice and convertibility is one of the many flexible features of many such annuities.

The Swiss Banking System

Unimpressed with economic policies bordering on insanity, embraced by the rest of the world, traditional Swiss economic policy is dictated by adherence to prudent fiscal principles. No better confirmation of this truth can be cited than the Swiss banking system and its enviable history. While this banking record does not bear directly on the wisdom of investing in Swiss insurance annuities it is worth noting as further evidence of the general atmosphere of stability in which such investments are made and protected.

The elite Swiss franc is very much at home in our unique national banking system which reflects our national values. Created as the central bank in 1907, the Swiss National Bank controls the currency supply. Unlike most other central banks our National Bank is a joint stock company and any Swiss citizen can own shares which are traded on the Swiss stock exchange. We have already described the statutory requirement for the franc's gold backing, a restriction which dictates the central bank's historic policy of maintaining a slow and stable growth of the money supply.

Switzerland has more than 5,000 banks and they are among the safest anywhere. There are only four AAA-rated banks in the world and three of them are in Switzerland. Bank failure is extremely rare and actual loss to depositors almost never has occurred. While the primary source of bank deposits is domestic, the funds of foreign depositors are equal or greater. In no other nation are bank deposits more than double the national gross domestic product. It is worth repeating that the combined total assets of Swiss banks exceed Sfr. 1000 billion (US$400 billion) but funds under management for clients on a fiduciary or trustee basis exceeds that amount many times over.

Swiss banks have also become one of the world's most important institutions for international capital flow. As managers of their clients' funds the three largest Swiss banks, Credit Suisse, Swiss Bank Corporation and Union Bank of Switzerland rank among the leading investors in world finance.

Swiss banks are strictly supervised by the Federal Banking Commission with regular exacting and complex audits, a strong protection for depositors. There has never been a need for a Swiss equivalent of the U.S. Federal Deposit Insurance Corporation (FDIC) to bailout failing institutions. By law bank liquidity and capital resource levels are the highest in the world at about 100%, twice that required, for example, in the United States.

The Banking Acting of 1934

It was the French prelate-statesman Cardinal Richelieu who said: "Secrecy is the first essential in the affairs of state." We Swiss believe this sentiment is best applied to personal financial affairs.

The Swiss Banking Act of 1934 enacted into federal law our centuries-old reputation for discretion and privacy. This law provides far more than a promise of total secrecy in financial matters. Divulging any client's financial secrets is a criminal act and bank officers or employees can be punished by up to six months imprisonment and a fine of Sfr. 30,000. This secrecy requirement does not end with bank employment but goes with the employee to his grave.

The rise to power of Adolf Hitler in Germany in 1933 was rightfully viewed in Switzerland as a real threat to our independence. The 1934 banking law was enacted to stop Nazi agents from bribing bank employees for information concerning the Swiss accounts of German citizens and expatriates but it still works today protecting foreign depositors from unwarranted intrusions into their banking privacy from any source. Our government has steadfastly defended banking secrecy in more recent times even against great foreign pressure to abandon it, usually from the official agencies of other governments. As I noted, this bank secrecy has been endorsed strongly by the Swiss electorate in referendum.

An increasingly valuable currency, a solid experienced international banking system, statutory maximum financial privacy; these unique Swiss factors combine to create a climate in which an investor can have the highest degree of confidence, a situation unequaled elsewhere in the world.

Why Invest Abroad?

Although it would be in their own best financial interest, unfortunately many Americans do not have an international view when considering where to place investments. Most Americans have their jobs, their homes, their pensions and virtually all of their investments in the United States although the U.S. economy accounts for only about one third of the world economy. Knowledgeable investors realize that international exposure for long-term investment portfolios can be healthy and profitable, so much so that some financial experts suggest 20% to 50% of investments should be abroad.

Aside from the stability and good return Swiss investments in general guarantee, there are very strong U.S. domestic reasons why an American citizen, or anyone with investments in America, should consider putting assets into a Swiss annuity.

The state of the U.S. economy is very important to an investor, whether or not he is an American. Many people around the world have used the U.S. dollar as a repository for their wealth, and the economies of many countries are affected by what happens in America. It is easy to be blinded by traditional faith in the value of the dollar and belief in America as a place to protect wealth based on long past history. But it is critical to any investor not to live in the past but to carefully assess the truth about the American economy today. You want your investment to be as safe as possible and that requires analyzing the current state of the U.S. economy in the same way that a stock analyst would examine a large corporation. Or look at the United States as you would a foreign country in which you are considering placing your assets or investments. From this perspective the question becomes not whether you should diversify by going international but, "where and how much?"

First there are the social indicators of instability. More than 33 million Americans - 13.5% of the population, are officially living in poverty, up 20% in the last decade. More than 24,000 Americans were murdered last year, which was a new record. The prison population has doubled to one million in the last decade. In other words, one in every 270 Americans is in jail (the highest rate in the world).

America is now spending about 1% of its Gross National Product on infrastructure: roads, railways, bridges, water systems, etc. - one of the lowest figures for capital projects expenditure in the industrialized world.

With the 1993 adoption of President Clinton's budget package, America's total public debt exceeded more than $4 trillion (that's $4,000,000,000,000) and is growing. The Clinton budget plan alone authorized increases in the national debt to $5.5 trillion. That debt is increasing at the nearly incomprehensible rate of $20,000 per second every minute of every day, more than $400 billion a year. In 1992 the interest the American government (taxpayers) paid on that debt was $295 billion - 62 cents out of every dollar paid in income taxes went to debt service.

The current administration in Washington, D.C., may not be able to spend as much as it would like -- no administration gets its entire budget approved -- but it is clear that during the Clinton years much higher government spending than ever before is going forward. The trend is under way, and Americans seem to be once again convinced they can spend their way out of recession.

In the private sector America's corporate debt ratio compared to earnings is around $1.90 for every $1 produced by the U.S. economy.

In 1990 the median income of Americans fell for the first time since 1982. The U.S. economy, after a relatively "soft landing" from the 1980's boom, is now engaged in sluggish struggle to rise from the doldrums. Average job creation from 1989 to 1992 was the lowest since the 1930's.

There are deepening anxieties -- not all shared by all, but all felt by many -- about health care, education, crime, poverty, business and public investment, the federal deficit and the savings and loans debacle.

Numerous companies, large and small, have cut hundreds of thousands of workers from payrolls and more reductions are planned. Manufacturing jobs are not the only ones under threat. General Motors is cutting at least 74,000 jobs, but companies with large white-collar work forces, such as IBM, American Express and Travellers' Insurance, are also cutting thousands from their staffs. Much of this is described as necessary "restructuring" towards a new type of economy but that kind of wishful phrase can hide the deep fault lines in America's economic standing.

Impressive statistics can be gathered to show that America's capacity to sustain its own strength -- in terms of educational standards, health care, crime, poverty, investment in infrastructure and industry -- is quietly slipping away. Quietly, because there seems to be little national will to address these problems, much less acknowledge their existence.

One study shows that only 30% of U.S. employers believe school graduates are literate and numerate; but 70% of students and 65% of parents think their schools are fine. This points to the core problem with U.S. education: low intensity, in all but sport, and low expectations, for all but the brightest students in honors classes.

The nightmarish complexity and bureaucratic waste of the public health programs for the poor and old in the U.S., Medicaid and Medicare, are exceeded only by the complexity and waste of the private health insurance sector. The cost of private health insurance, mostly borne by industry, is doubling every seven years.

What is more significant is that health is now a common middle-class headache for the first time. Employers are forcing their employees to contribute more and take less generous benefits; the high cost of insurance squeezes wages; people who have a poor health history, even if fully cured, find themselves locked into their jobs, because prospective new employers refuse to take them on.

Now looming on the political agenda are plans for a comprehensive national "health care system" rivaling Great Britain's dismal "socialized medicine" experiment in scope and cost. Many believe this added government control of an industry which comprises one fifth of the American economy can only mean higher taxes and reduced quality of medical care for everyone.

The nature of the 1994 U.S. tax increases is instructive. With a top marginal rate now increased to 39.6% the top earners are saddled with a hundred billion or more in new taxes. This soak-the-rich scheme has two goals: to raise money for new programs and to begin again equalizing income distribution which used to be called socialism. Apparently American politicians and the public have forgotten that such confiscatory taxes reduce incentives and produce more evasion than revenues.

Move on to the "spend" side of the liberal "tax-spend-and-elect" philosophy. As noted these proposals include a vast expansion of the health care system, more money for education and a huge program of infrastructure projects.

There are also plans for "a national economic strategy" which would make even a Fascist dictator blush. President Clinton plans to use government (tax) money to finance a "co-operative relationship" with those U.S. industries his bureaucrats think constitute the wave of the future. Even Ford, Chrysler and General Motors have surrendered to federal government control and subsidy for joint production of a "wonder car." Such programs inevitably, in practice, degenerate into efforts to shore up dying industries in perceived politically important areas where votes can be gained. While hopefully all this Utopia will not come to pass, what is important to the wise investor is the philosophy that has been adopted by the American government and the resulting economic direction which may produce a disaster.

From a neutral vantage point it appears that there is much official deception in all these plans. Costs that U.S. taxpayers don't want to bear are hidden by loading them on to businesses. Already groaning under an estimated $115 billion annual bill for pollution control, businesses will be forced to take on still higher clean-up costs. And American businesses may be forced to provide health care to employees not now covered, at an annual cost variously estimated at $50 to $100 billion. There is talk of a business tax equal to 1.5% of payrolls to finance the training of lower-level employees. These plans may not all happen, but some form of further tax increase will, and any part of these programs adds costs that are economically destructive. All this will, of course, force businesses to raise prices, making them less competitive in world markets and impairing the investment value of their securities.

However easy for many to believe, such tax, spending and government control policies are economically impossible to achieve. For the investor, what is important is not how the policies are packaged in high-sounding words, but what the true consequences are going to be, especially on investments you hold in the United States.

The problem comes in trying to raise taxes to pay for all this. It is not that the American government minds raising taxes, especially on "the rich." Most dispiriting of all, judging by their reported statements, is the number of businessmen who expect economic leadership from government, as if the U.S. were a single concern managed by a White House Five Year Plan. Does one have to say yet again that no matter how much governments spend, lasting economic growth comes from the efforts of individuals and businesses responding to market demand and technological opportunity? At the very time that the former Communist countries are moving towards a free market, Americans have given national power to an administration which wants the government to have more control over business and the economy.

Forgive my saying so, but Americans should have grown out of this economic immaturity by now -- but they haven't -- and the consequences must be dealt with by all investors.

The combined result of the government attitude and this belief by so many businessmen can quickly erode investment values even further.

I am aware that economic alarmism has been a popular (and profitable) pasttime for many. But perhaps too many people have been crying "wolf" for too long. Each tremor in the U.S. stock market, the commodities market, or the gold market has been widely expected to lead to depression. Books on the coming collapse were very popular, and then became discredited when nothing happened. There has never been a shortage of economic doom sayers. They were frequently joined by hard-headed industrialists who wanted cheap money and plenty of it.

Another reason for being skeptical of the prophets of doom is that they have been dominated by fears of a repeat of the 1930's Depression, when U.S. national income fell by a third in real terms and the value of world trade fell by two thirds. There can be depressions, such as those of the 1870's in Europe and the 1890's in Britain, which are a good deal worse than the post-Second World War recessions, but which stop short of anything seen in the 1930's.

Meanwhile, American government seems to be reversing itself on policies such as de-regulation, curbs on union power, marginal tax cuts, privatization and a greater role for markets.

As economic illusions crumble, the situation for the investor can only get worse. An investor can stay in and ride with the storm, or can protect his family and the ideals in which he believes, and then be in a financial position to take whatever other actions he wishes.

International diversification is an important element of that investment protection.

The Depression Mentality

Despite the fact that they're earning an average return of under 3%, millions of Americans are allowing nearly $4 trillion of their financial assets to languish in domestic money market funds, bank certificates of deposit and short-term U.S. Treasury instruments.

The overwhelming majority of that money is held by two classes of people: (1) older Americans with a clear personal memory of the Depression, and (2) their children. The latter group (those born between, say, 1938 and 1950) may be too young to remember the horror of the Depression. But their attitudes toward money and risk come from parents who lived through (and never got over) those terrible years. Which explains why one keeps running into 45-year-olds with all their money in fixed-income investments. Though born in 1947, the year stocks began the great 22-year postwar bull market, these investors don't understand or appreciate their life experiences. They're victims of their parents' Depression-ravaged unconscious.

The Depression wrongly taught people that there was only one economic good; preservation of principal *as an end in itself.* By this logic, there was one risk; losing your money.

Which, in the absence of some "guarantee," these folks regard not just as a risk but as a virtual certainty.

The difficulty is, the Depression was a complete and total anomaly: a relatively brief, though acutely horrific, moment of deflation in a world of permanent decline in purchasing power (a/k/a inflation). And if an investor gets his definitions from an anomaly, as the owners of the $4 trillion in domestic investments most assuredly did, their resulting investment decisions are simply wrong.

Capital loss, while it will always be a risk, is not *the* risk. The overwhelming financial risk in American life today is extinction of purchasing power; the risk that an investor will outlive his income, then outlive his principal, and still not be even remotely dead.

Principal has no intrinsic value, in other words. It is only worth the purchasing power of the income stream it produces. This is a total abstraction to the children of deflation, to whom principal is a sacred thing. And, in order to preserve principal, these people continue to make only investments that, net of inflation and taxes, usually return zero or less.

In a world of constantly rising costs of living, the children of deflation invest so that their purchasing power is constantly eroded away. They call their mode of investing "safe." In fact "suicidal" is a more accurate word. In a rising cost world, investing for capital preservation alone (at the expense of purchasing power) is the ultimate recklessness. Oddly most Americans do not seem to even be aware that this is going on in their country. We wonder how this can be. Can the land of the free have gone so far off course?

Swiss financial managers recall all too well the excesses of the several German regimes prior to the Second World War, and are very distressed by the financial horror stories that now arrive from America.

An Equal Threat: the Litigation Explosion

There is yet another major reason for Americans to invest internationally as a means to protect their assets.

If someone slips and falls in a store, or if an auto taps another auto's rear end, many Americans react like they just won the lottery. If an armed thug breaks into a home in the dead of night, slips on a child's marbles, and breaks a leg, he can sue and likely win.

Once there a court judgment is obtained to compensate the "victim," the court swears the defendant in and takes their testimony "in aid of collection." The "guilty" party has to tell the court *everything*, no matter how unjust the charges against him may have been. At this stage the case is over, and the only thing to discuss is where the assets are to pay the judgment. What properties the defendant may own, what savings accounts, what checking accounts, and what money market funds, and how much is in each one. What stocks they own, what bonds they own, where each and every safe deposit box is and what precisely they have in each.

Under American criminal law the accused has certain rights, such as a right to silence. But as a judgment debtor in a civil collection proceeding a person has no rights; the winner now owns everything. If the debtor conceals a safe deposit box, or that stash of ten Krugerrands he buried ten years ago in the garden, he's committing perjury, a felony. With mandatory sentencing guidelines in effect in most jurisdictions, the perjurer will go to prison for the amount of time specified in the statute, since the judge no longer has the discretion but must sentence in accordance with the guidelines created by the legislature for that crime. The popular concept of probation for a first offense is no longer true in many jurisdictions, including the federal court system, which abolished it for crimes after 1987. The perjury defendant may even spend more time in prison than the thug who broke into his house and slipped on his child's marbles. While the defendant's lying about his assets will always be the felony of perjury, if the thug walked into the house in daylight through an unlocked door, his crime is likely to be the misdemeanor of trespass, with a maximum sentence of six months, versus the perjury felony with a maximum of from five to twenty years, depending upon the jurisdiction.

It is all too easy to go around saying it won't happen, but once it happens to you, it is too late. If money is transferred after an incident or accident, that is concealing assets, which can cause both criminal charges and civil loss of other assets. The U.S. law looks at it as stealing the property of the person who is suing, or who may sue. The defendant may think it is his lifetime savings from hard work, but legally he now holds it in trust for the person who has even a pending unproven claim. Presumed knowledge of the possibility of a claim is sufficient to invoke these fraudulent transfer laws. So if somebody moves their money the morning after an auto accident, it is likely to come back to haunt them. Such an act can result in criminal charges, and increase the amount of the civil judgment, since the plaintiff can claim the extra costs incurred by deliberate evasion of the judgment. The only legally valid protection is to take careful and legal protective steps well in advance of a potential claim against a person or his assets.

While these valid concerns with protecting assets obviously apply to Americans, citizens of any nationality need to consider the current dangers of keeping bank accounts or other assets in America. Such trends also raises serious concerns about the viability of investments in American businesses whose value might be affected by such litigation.

Lessons of History

The history of U.S. economic policy for most of this century supports the view that even in America, the world's one supposed bastion of capitalism, inflationary economic policies are the natural consequences of government's tendency toward accumulation of ever more power and the need to finance its political schemes. From 1965 to the end of World War I the U.S. was a pioneer's land moving from strength to strength while creating wealth at a then unprecedented rate. In July, 1919, the U.S. dollar reached its highest value against the Swiss franc and has been declining ever since. The British pound sterling has suffered a similar fate. The wise investor sees the need to escape from such inflationary policy. He or she also knows one of the best hedges is having a portion of one's wealth safely diversified abroad.

There is of course the normal desire to stay with what we know most intimately. Each of us lives in a nation to which our allegiance is naturally inclined and whose social and cultural environment has influenced our thinking. Some will brand foreign investment as some sort of disloyalty. They are wrong.

All nations are not equal and among those who are safest from an investment viewpoint Switzerland stands head and shoulders above the rest. We have already enumerated the solid facts behind this statement but mine is a practical, not patriotic opinion. Those whose business is dispassionate economic analysis agree. According to the International Country Risk Guide, Switzerland (91.5 score out of a possible 100) is the safest nation out of 129 surveyed counting political, financial and other risks for investment. The United States ranked 10th (score of 83.5), well behind even Luxembourg, Norway, Austria, Germany, the Netherlands, Brunei, Japan and Singapore.

While international investing will require you to develop a sophistication about the laws, taxes and events in another country such calculations are not too different from investment comparisons you must make among U.S. companies and other possible domestic investment opportunities. What you gain is safety, guaranteed return, privacy, reduced taxes and escape from political events which could rapidly destroy your assets and your way of life.

Swiss Investment Management

Swiss investment managers are experienced in working with investors from around the world. Most are fluent in English and have substantial experience in managing various types of investments. They are comfortable managing an investor's entire portfolio if he wishes; however, for investors who prefer to make their own financial decisions,

Swiss advisers are happy to offer their expertise to the degree it is required. They can help you manage your investments, or manage them for you - whichever arrangement makes you feel more comfortable. For the entrepreneur who devotes much of his energy to building his venture, the efficiency and competence of Swiss investment managers can be a major attraction.

A fine example of a Swiss money management company is Weber Hartmann Vrijhof & Partners. Offering management services for the portfolios of both individuals and companies, the firm excels at providing personal attention to its clients. Weber Hartmann Vrijhof & Partners was established in 1992 and offers specialized investment services designed to meet the individual needs of their clients.

The minimum opening portfolio to be managed by this firm is $200,000 or equivalent. It is not feasible to manage an account of less than this as the transaction costs and inability to properly diversify would not allow a proper service to the client. The management team here normally recommends that a portion of the portfolio be invested in hard currencies other than the U.S. dollar including the Swiss franc, French franc, German mark, and Dutch guilder. Respected for their conservative approach to portfolio management, the partners assist clients with opening a custodial account at one of the major private Swiss banks, so that all client securities are held by the bank, not the investment manager.

A large percentage of their clients are based in the United States. One of their main goals has always been to get a certain portion of their clients' wealth out of the U.S. dollar and into European hard currencies such as Swiss francs,

Deutschmarks, and Dutch guilders, and then build a portfolio with a mix of bonds and shares.

The Zurich-based executives you would be dealing with are Robert Vrijhof and René Schatt.

Robert Vrijhof began his banking career in 1978 with the Union Bank of Switzerland, working his way through the international securities trading department. Later, with Credit Suisse, he held the senior position as manager of the Foreign Stock Exchange trading section. In 1987, he accepted an offer by Foreign Commerce Bank as portfolio manager. His profound knowledge in this area soon led to the position of Vice-President and head of the portfolio management group at Focobank.

René Schatt started his banking career in 1977 with the Thurgauer Cantonalbank, where he finished his basic training. In 1984, he joined the Foreign Commerce Bank and worked his way through the securities administration and trading department. At the same time, he continued studying and in 1987, he achieved the "Federal Diploma of Banking Expert." In 1990, he was promoted to Vice-President and head of the securities department. In 1992, he joined the first Korean Bank in Switzerland, KDB Bank (Switzerland) Ltd., working as Senior Vice-President and being the Swiss Member of the General Management.

If you wish to learn more about the services the firm offers, contact them at:

Weber Hartmann Vrijhof & Partners, Ltd.
Attn: New Clients Department
Zurichstrasse 110B
CH-8134 Adilswil
Switzerland
Tel: +41 1 709-11-15
Fax: +41 1 709-11-13, please mark fax "Attn: New Clients Department"

or you may use their online inquiry form at http://www.cyberhaven.com/whvp/

Even though many investors recognize that Switzerland is a center of finance and investment, they do not realize the vast scope of the investment options offered by Swiss financial institutions and companies. Switzerland is a prime spot for investment for numerous reasons, most importantly for the strength of its currency, security of its financial system, and steady returns on investment.

The Swiss Insurance Industry:

The World's Safest Insurance Center

Lloyd's of London is an ancient and venerable, though now somewhat shaky, insurance company romantically depicted in motion pictures and novels as the daring international insurer of great merchant ships plying stormy seas or the delicate fingers of renowned concert pianists.

Too few people realize that relatively unglamorous Switzerland is actually the most important insurance center in the world. It is here the world's largest re-insurance company (the insurance companies' insurance company), Swiss Re-Insurance, is located. To a degree unequalled anywhere else Swiss policyholders are protected by insurance companies with the world's unquestionably safest records of operation.

Since 1885 the Swiss Constitution (Article 34) has dictated uniform federal supervision of private insurance companies. The Swiss Federal Bureau for Private Insurance (FOPI) strictly watches over the national insurance industry applying some of the most stringent laws and regulations in force today in any nation; and the companies themselves willingly pay the government's supervisory expenses. Even in individualistic Switzerland no other segment of business operates under tighter rules. The result: in the 132-year history of our insurance industry no company has ever been forced to cease operations, gone bankrupt nor has any company failed to meet its full obligations. Forgive me if I suggest that strict regulation alone is not the reason for this enviable record although that is important; the Swiss qualities of sobriety, prudence and financial conservatism also play an important part.

There are only twenty Swiss insurance companies ranging from Swiss Life & Pension founded in 1857 to the newest, Phoenix Life, founded in 1978. The companies vary widely in total assets but the crucial factor for you is which one best provides the personal service you want. The FOPI scrutinizes each company to protect depositors from overcharges or under-performance. High-yield, risky investments are not allowed and the rate of return differs little from one company and to another. There is some difference in dividends paid but competition keeps that small as well.

The FOPI insists companies invest their funds in broad-based and profitable portfolios to avoid overexposure in any single area of investment. By law, insurance companies are limited to investing in Swiss government bonds, Swiss real estate, mortgages, and not to exceed 5% of their portfolios in securities. All insurance company funds must remain in Switzerland. Most insurance investments are in Swiss gilt-edged bonds and prime real estate (which since 1989 by law cannot exceed 30% of a company's total investments). For example a leading Swiss all around insurer with which I often work, Elvia Life, founded in 1924, has more than 225,000 clients, at least half abroad. In 1992 Elvia allocated its assets as follows: 53.7% in Swiss bonds and secured loans; 25.5% in mortgages on Swiss real estate; 16.3% in real estate ownership; and 4.5% in Swiss stocks. Bonds are routinely carried on insurance company books at current market value, not cost, whereas real estate loans are valued at cost, often less than half of their current market value. This is more evidence of our conservative Swiss approach, in this case providing a protective price cushion factored into portfolios to shelter investors in the unlikely event of a Swiss real estate market collapse. On average Swiss real estate is the most highly valued in Europe.

In the light of the widespread financial difficulties faced in recent years by the U.S. and other national insurance industries consider for a moment a 1992 Swiss insurance company audit reported by The Financial Times of London. To test how the Swiss insurer would measure up to new, more liberal auditing standards adopted by the European Community (EC), three auditing methods were employed to measure the company's shareholder equity. The results were as follows: 1) using traditional Swiss (FOPI) standards shareholder equity was found to be Sfr. 2.66 billion; 2) under prevailing European audit standards it was Sfr. 3.70 billion; 3) under the new EC accounting standards the result was Sfr. 4.64 billion in equity. It is likely any of the nineteen other Swiss companies would have produced similar audit results. These comparative figures demonstrate the traditional Swiss insurance company practice of under-estimating true net worth as a hedge against possible inflation or international economic problems. This practice means that in the event of a worldwide economic collapse Swiss insurance companies could lose up to half their book value and still continue to meet all their financial obligations.

U.S. Insurance Problems

With no criticism intended, it is useful to contrast the Swiss insurance system with the U.S. insurance industry and its recent situation. Though the facts have not received wide public notice comparable to the savings and loan scandals, American insurance companies suffer from similar problems. In the last decade 226 U.S. insurance companies operating in more than one state have failed and more than 200 single state companies have also collapsed, many from fraud and other questionable practices.

Risky investments and a declining reliance on premiums as a major share of income have pushed about one third of the top 100 American companies into a shaky status which could become acute in the event of a major recession. Companies such as Executive Life of California and Executive Life of New York, both subsidiaries of First Executive Corporation were taken over by New York state regulators in 1991. First Capital Life Insurance, a subsidiary of First Capital Holdings, 28% owned by Shearson Lehman Brothers, was taken over by California regulators in 1991 and another subsidiary, Fidelity Bankers Life Insurance Company was placed in receivership in Virginia. Monarch Life Insurance of Massachusetts also collapsed in 1991. Perhaps the most disturbing event occurred in July, 1991, when the New Jersey Department of Insurance took over Mutual Benefit Life Insurance Company, the fourth oldest company in America founded in 1845 and the 18th largest mutual life company. Insurance company rating services have even downgraded the financial standing of major U.S. companies such as John Hancock, Principal Mutual, Travelers, Aetena and Mutual of New York (MONY). In 1993 the securities division of

Prudential and the Metropolitan Life both admitted to fraud against clients in misrepresenting investment and insurance plans.

In 1970 over 90% of U.S. insurance company income was earned from premium payments. By 1990 only 34% of all companies' income came from premiums and 60% from investments not unlike those which brought down the savings and loan industry; speculative commercial real estate and junk bonds. Another continuing problem has been the lack of national uniform insurance company regulation since each of the United States provide their own degree of scrutiny. For example state insurance regulatory officials in Louisiana, North Carolina and Wyoming were subjected to state and federal criminal charges in 1991 based on the operations of their offices.

How Swiss Insurance Companies Make Money

The former prime minister of Great Britain, Lady Margaret Thatcher, told The Spectator of London in a 1980 interview: "No one would remember the Good Samaritan if he had only good intentions. He had money as well."

Fortunately for you, the Swiss insurance industry has both.

As in any other business, insurance rates differ among the 20 Swiss companies because some are more successful than others in their management techniques. Every franc they take in goes to 1) overhead and administration; 2) a set aside for "death risk" payments in event of premature death of the insured; 3) a savings portion which is invested in order to increase the cash value of the insurance policy and allow dividends. Overhead can be kept low, death risk can be re-insured with other companies to spread the risk and conservative life expectancy tables can be used to raise premiums. As we have seen, by Swiss law prudent investment for profit must be solidly placed in non-risky areas. Nevertheless within this circumscribed operating universe Swiss insurance companies manage to make respectable profits and a good rate of return for their investors.

Advantages of Swiss Insurance

Aside from the continuing strength of the Swiss franc there are several additional and very attractive features which come with ownership of Swiss insurance:

- Competitive Interest and Dividends: Added to the appreciating value of the franc, Swiss annuities pay regular guaranteed interest and dividends higher than that paid for Swiss bank accounts. Swiss law requires each insurance company to pay a minimum of 3% annual interest on the savings or reserve portion of your annuity and traditionally policyholders are also paid a portion of investment profits as dividends. In recent years, depending on the company, dividends range from 0.5% to 1.5% above the guaranteed 3% with the total ranging from 3.5% to 4.5% on average. Your interest income is credited to your annuity cash reserve but also increases your future life income. Compared to interest rate standards in some nations this may not be exciting, but remember such high interest rates reflect currency inflation which in Switzerland has been historically low. Though it is often forgotten by those unfortunate enough to live in inflationary countries, inflation and interest rates are a true barometer of the basic soundness of a nation's economy and currency. Comparatively lower Swiss interest rates mirror your low risk in any Swiss investment you make.

Methods of Dividend Distribution

It is important for you to know that all Swiss insurance companies do not follow the same method of distribution when it comes to paying dividends. You should be careful to examine and choose the method best suited to your needs. Before I give you a brief summary of the various distribution methods you should also know there is no need for potential annuity buyers to go "shopping" from one Swiss company to another comparing plans and checking possible interest and dividends before making a decision on your own. This once prevalent method was not only time consuming but often frustrating because of language differences.

My investment counseling company, whose staff speaks English, listens carefully as you describe exactly what you want to achieve with your annuity plan. Once we know what you want and how much you wish to invest, we find the best annuity for you at the company which best suits your needs in every respect. You pay nothing for this service. Brokers are compensated by the insurance company, which is pleased to pay commissions to brokers who bring in new business and make their lives simpler. Our company is proud to have arranged for tailor-made insurance for many thousands of foreign buyers and we will be glad to assist you.

Before we evaluate the dividend distribution methods keep in mind these factors: 1) Declining interest rates come with decreased inflation. Decreased Swiss inflation means the Swiss franc will appreciate, which for you means a greater rate of return convertible in your own national currency; 2) Rising interest rates produce a higher investment yield for your insurance company and this can mean higher dividend payments to you as the annuity holder.

Declining Dividends: Under this method dividends are paid out as a percentage of your annuity's reserve on the date your annuity life income begins. Over the period when the income is paid to you the established reserves under your annuity contract decrease and so do your dividends. Eventually dividends cease completely. The only advantage to this method is you can obtain an immediate high dividend payout.

"New money" Dividends: Here dividends are calculated based on the insurance company's investment return at the time you purchase your annuity. (The "new money" refers to a first time premium payment). Once this purchase date dividend rate is imposed it stays fixed for the annuity's specified number of years, much like the interest rate in a "fixed rate" mortgage in the United States. If Swiss interest rates rise or fall, new insurance contracts issued in each period vary up or down accordingly but are still fixed on the date of purchase. Frankly I believe this method contains a built-in unfairness to insurance buyers. Why should dividend rates differ based on the time of purchase? If your insurance company increases its earnings after you purchase your annuity you should be able to share in that profitability and not be tied to an artificially low dividend rate. Obviously if a time comes, unlike the present, when the prospect is for long-term declines in interest rates this fixed "new money" dividend method could be to your advantage. That time doesn't seem likely soon.

Equal Dividend Payments: The fairest and most reasonable dividend method, I believe, is one which provides all annuity or other policyholders with the same dividend return rate regardless of when they purchased their contract. This is the method used by U.S. insurance companies in distributing dividends and it is available from Swiss companies as well.

Asset Protection: Under Swiss law the value of an insurance policy or annuity is protected against any legal collection procedures brought by the policyholder's creditors. A Swiss insurance policy or annuity does not have to be included as an asset in filing bankruptcy in Switzerland or elsewhere. With certain annuity provisions you can choose (a member of your family is the named beneficiary) your annuity is even immune from any foreign court orders or judgments so long as you purchased it before filing bankruptcy.

Limited Tax Reporting Required: Unlike opening a Swiss bank account (the existence of which is reportable by law to the U.S. Internal Revenue Service) U.S. citizens are not required to report to any U.S. agency their ownership of, or the accumulated interest and dividend earnings from a foreign insurance policy or annuity. As you will see below in my discussion of U.S. tax rules on foreign annuities, the U.S. does impose an excise tax at purchase and income taxes upon annuity payments but the policyholder is not compelled to tell the I.R.S. what kind of annuity he has or where he bought it.

No Taxes on Earnings: While interest earnings on Swiss bank accounts or other investments are subject to a 35% Swiss federal withholding tax, accumulated interest earnings on insurance annuities are tax free in Switzerland and not subject to United States income taxes during the deferral period before pay back begins. Once annuity income is paid or upon liquidation of the annuity U.S. income taxes are payable.

According to the U.S. Internal Revenue Code the amount of the total premium paid for the annuity (in U.S. dollars) is divided by the life expectancy (number of years) for the age of the person insured when the annuity payment begins. The dollar amount thus calculated is tax free. For example: A 65-year-old American invests US$10,000 in a Swiss annuity. The non-taxable part of his yearly annuity income (which begins under his policy immediately) equals the $10,000 divided by a 15-year life expectancy; that is $666.67. So if he received US$850 in annuity payments the first year, only $183.33 ($850 less $666.67) would be reportable and taxable as ordinary income. If however the value of the Swiss franc increases in the second year so that the annuity pays him US$950, the taxable portion would be $283.33 ($950 less $666.67).

It also should be noted that under U.S. tax law there is a one-time 1% excise tax based on the amount of your original investment in foreign insurance which on a $10,000 annuity would be $100. U.S. taxpayers are required by law to report the fact of a foreign insurance purchase and pay the tax using I.R.S. Excise Tax Return Form 720.

Remember also that any capital invested in a Swiss annuity is not included as part of your personal estate when you die. Varying with the amount you invest in the annuity, this avoidance of U.S. death and inheritance taxes can mean a huge savings for your heirs as annuity beneficiaries. As the British economist John Maynard Keynes said: "The avoidance of taxes is the only pursuit that still carries any reward."

Pension Plan Convertability: Corporate or self-employment U.S. pension plans or individual retirement accounts (IRAs or Keogh) can legally invest in and hold title to Swiss annuities or be rolled over into Swiss annuities which are far more secure and profitable than many other investments.

Estate Planning: The ownership of Swiss insurance annuities (as compared to the person insured) can be changed easily by the policyholder by written notice at any time with no legal formalities. If the annuity is owned by a person (rather than a corporation, trust or other entity which can also purchase annuities) when the annuity holder dies a new owner can be named without proof of a will, use of a power of attorney or probate or other court procedures.

Secrecy: The same criminal and civil penalties for violations of a client's privacy imposed on all Swiss bank officials and employees also apply to insurance company workers for life.

Immunity from Exchange Controls: When a national government imposes exchange controls it often requires its citizens known to have foreign bank accounts to repatriate their money held abroad. A review of historic exchange controls, even the strictest, imposed by various nations shows that insurance policies held abroad are exempt from repatriation. It is well established in the legal systems of both civil and common law nations that an insurance annuity or policy is a mutual contract between the insured and the issuing company which takes precedence over any governmental claims on a citizen's assets.

Instant Liquidity of Funds: With many Swiss annuities you can make a lump sum deposit and immediately borrow up to 90% of the cash value at Swiss commercial interest rates, a net interest rate of only 0.5%. The insurance company itself does not make such loans but the annuity contract can be used as collateral for a bank loan.

No "Load Fees": Investing in a Swiss annuity is on a "no load" basis with no initial or back-end fees charged. There are no sales or administrative fees charged. All costs are included in the insurance company's rates. Without loss of principal your investment can be canceled at any time and with all principal, interest and dividends due payable if you cancel more than one year after purchase.

Ease of Payment: You can make deposits on your Swiss annuity with the same ease as mailing an insurance premium at your local post box. Your payment can be made by check or wire in your national or any currency drawn on your local or other bank account or by standing bank order. Premium payments do not have to be exact in amount but approximate allowing for the convertability of your currency into Swiss francs. You also can establish your own deposit account with the insurance company itself from which periodic payments can be made. Unlike Anglo-American insurance companies Swiss insurance companies offer a wide range of banking services in connection with their insurance services. Such insurance accounts are not considered "bank" accounts under Swiss law and there is no tax imposed or need to report under U.S. I.R.S. rules.

You can choose to receive your annuity income payments each year, every six months or each quarter. Monthly payments are available only to Swiss residents.

Although the amount of your annuity income is denominated in Swiss francs you can elect to receive actual payment in any currency you wish and the insurance company will make the conversion for you. Payments can be made to you at a bank you designate anywhere in the world. Remember all these transactions are private and by Swiss law kept secret unless you order otherwise.

Most annuities you may purchase allow you to begin receiving your income earlier than originally planned but this will reduce the payment amounts. You may also defer receiving income longer than originally planned and this will increase the eventual payments. Should you wish to add funds to your annuities a new contract can be signed with the company and when the deferral date arrives all of the contracts will be combined and administered as one annuity.

Preparing for the Future: Swiss Insurance Annuities

Which Swiss Annuity Is Best for You?

The ultimate purpose of all investing is consumption. If tomorrow the dollar, pound or franc you invested today is worth less your purpose has been thwarted. The Swiss annuity is one of the few investment choices which consistently has delivered the increasing purchasing power needed to meet today's financial needs.

An annuity is simply a lifetime income guaranteed by an insurance company. The purpose of the annuity is to remove the pecuniary danger of "living too long." If your assets are gone before you are there has been a miscalculation of the balance between accumulation and consumption. The same predicament results when your national currency inflation erodes your buying power. The Swiss annuity solves these twin problems by giving you a guaranteed income for life paid to you in a currency with an historic record of not only maintaining but increasing its purchasing power.

In countries such as the United States, familiar "annuities" come in two forms; "fixed annuities" such as certificates of deposit (CDs) earning a fixed interest rate for a set period of time, or; "variable annuities" producing fluctuating income based on a basket of investment accounts including stocks and bonds. While some similarities do exist,

Swiss insurance annuities differ significantly from such U.S. investment devices, principally by being virtually risk-free. Unlike the situation in the United States Swiss annuities are not placed in peril by unsound or failing insurance companies with shaky investments. As we have discussed Swiss law does not permit this to occur.

Who Are the Parties to an Annuity?

It will be useful for tax and other purposes for you to consider the potential parties involved in the purchase of an annuity (or any insurance policy). A straight-life annuity can involve only one person. But other annuities may involve several parties. First, there is the insured, the person whose life is actually the subject of the insurance contract and whose death will trigger maturity of the contract and payment of benefits to beneficiaries. If the insured is not also the policyholder, he has no rights under the policy.

The policyholder owns the annuity and exercises full power to choose its terms, options, and appointment of beneficiaries in case of the insured's death. A policyholder can be a human individual but it can also be a legal entity such as a trust, a corporation, a bank, even a holding company (which can mean even greater tax savings in some nations).

The beneficiaries named by the policyholder can also be individuals or a legal entity.

Finally there is the payer of the premium and this also can be a person or a legal entity distinct from the insured or policyholder.

Because there are four possible parties to a Swiss annuity you may want to discuss with experts your nation's legal and tax ramifications to insure maximum benefit for you and the others to be involved.

Types of Annuities:

There are several variable factors which will affect the size of life income you create with any given premium you decide to pay among which are: whether you want the payments to begin immediately or at a future date; whether you alone or you and your spouse (or another person) are to be included, and; whether you wish to designate beneficiaries.

Swiss franc income annuities are ideal for a person at or nearing retirement, whatever his or her age may be, because they provide a guaranteed lifetime income.

This income annuity can be: immediate, usually for those who wish to retire now and make a lump sum payment producing lifetime income starting immediately, or; deferred, favored by those five or ten years away from retirement willing to defer income until they do retire. This is accomplished by either a lump sum payment or regular annual, biannual or quarterly (the most common) contributions. The deferred annuity is actually an accumulation annuity with guaranteed income at a future date. For the same premium a differed annuity will give you a greater life income than an immediate annuity. Bear in mind that in some cases it might be more profitable to purchase an immediate annuity and invest the income during the comparable deferred annuity period.

In either of these income annuities the policyholder obtains automatic life insurance coverage and benefits during the deferral phase.

Swiss annuities can be tailored by the company to your individual personal or family circumstances but here are three basic methods used to achieve desired ends:

1 "Without refund": This is what is sometimes called a "straight life income annuity" meaning the policyholder receives income for life but the contract ends with his or her death. This produces the largest lifetime income because there are no beneficiaries. It is suitable for a single person or one whose potential beneficiaries are already well protected by other means. If you are age 65 or older and have no immediate dependents or anyone who would suffer financial hardship without you a single straight life annuity would serve your needs. If the law in your country imposes a substantial death tax remember too that the funds you use to purchase this annuity are legally not part of your estate and escapes such taxes. For example a U.S. citizen investing $100,000 in such a policy would avoid about $30,000 in estate taxes. At the same time he provides himself an annual lifetime income based on the appreciating Swiss franc.

2 "10-Years-Certain": This annuity pays guaranteed income for your lifetime but should you die before the end of the ten-year term (or other fixed period of years you choose) these guaranteed payments will continue to your

beneficiaries until the agreed upon term of years expires.

3 "With Refund": In this annuity you receive income for life but upon your death the portion of your annuity already paid to you is subtracted from the original lump sum premium payment and the balance with interest is paid to your beneficiaries.

4 Joint and survivor option: A "single annuity" provides payment for one person so long as they live but a "joint annuity" can cover you and your spouse (or another person) until the last survivor dies. Both single and joint annuities can contain the "with refund" and "years certain" options for your beneficiaries as explained above. For a given premium amount two single annuities will offer a combined higher income than one joint annuity. However, if one spouse dies, the survivor has only his or her annuity income and even if spouse beneficiary provisions were contained in the deceased's annuity these will not equal the combination income of the two single annuities. For a higher premium payment you can choose a "joint and survivor" option which guarantees the surviving spouse a full or partial annuity for as long as they survive you.

Factors to Consider Before Choosing

Before you decide what type of annuity best serves your goals keep in mind several interrelated factors important to the success of your Swiss insurance plan. Some of these factors relate directly to established actuarial and statistical tables every insurance company employs in determining potential life span and thus premium costs; are you female or male; your age and the age of your spouse at the time you wish annuity income to begin; the amount of the initial or continuing deposit you can afford to make to the annuity. These factors determine how much you will have to pay and how much you, your spouse or your beneficiaries will be paid. These calculations should be fully explored before you decide which annuity to purchase.

Your age is crucial to this decision. The older you are the greater difference there will be in the income you receive from an "annuity without refund" as compared to an annuity with beneficiary options. For example at age 55 a man who invests in either an "annuity without refund" (explained above) or one with a beneficiary will receive about the same income under either option because at age 55 the life expectancy of either males or females is about the same. Based on statistics the insurance company probably will have to pay out the entire amount regardless of whether the annuity provides for no refund at death or for payment of the remainder to the surviving beneficiary.

The older the man is the more important the age factor becomes since it will determine the amount of income the company will pay out under either an "annuity without refund" (which provides more lifetime income) or one with a beneficiary (which gives less lifetime income). Similar variations would occur with a joint annuity including you and your spouse depending on your spouse's age.

These annuity choices should cause you to ask yourself:

- Who depends on me for their financial support and how long is this dependence likely to continue?
- Which annuity will best provide for my spouse and/or my children after my death?
- Is my spouse best protected by a joint annuity, an annuity with years certain, with refund or perhaps single annuities for each of us?

Other facts about you a Swiss insurance advisor will want to know is your employment status (self-employed, retired, corporate employee); whether you have an existing pension plan (IRA, Keogh, profit-sharing or other similar benefits); and whether your pension plan allows for lump sum distribution or not, which may be useful in conversion to a Swiss annuity.

One last point. Prospective buyers sometimes ask whether the insured needs a medical examination in order to buy an annuity and the answer is "no." The insurance company's risk is not based on the possibly poor state of the insured's health but on the risk that he or she may live "too long" and thereby receive more in income than was paid in the premium.

Insurance brokers such as myself or the individual insurance company will be pleased to provide you with complete tables showing exact premiums, annuity income and beneficiary pay outs available under each type of annuity and for various terms of years so that you may determine what is best suited to your needs.

Trusts vs. Swiss Annuities

Having considered the qualities of the Swiss insurance annuity it will be useful to review the intricacies of another common form of asset protection known in Anglo-American law as a "trust."

Asset protection planning is simply the process of organizing one' assets in advance to safeguard them from loss or dissipation because of potential risks. One method of protection can be found in a trust which severs legal and beneficial title to property by investing legal title in a trustee and equitable title in the beneficiary.

The trust is a popular but often complex legal device employed by citizens of English common law nations in order to achieve ends similar to those sought in purchasing a Swiss annuity. A trust can provide a lifetime income and control of the post mortem disposition of wealth in an advantageous way for the benefit of a spouse, child or other individual.

In its simplest definition a "trust" is a property interest held, used and/or cared for by one person for the benefit of another. The earliest known example is an Egyptian testamentary trust part of a will written in 1805 B.C. In the Middle Ages, when the Knights Templar acted as Paris-based international financiers, the trust was a common method used for royal and ecclesiastical investors who wished to shield their identity.

Over centuries the concept of the trust has been greatly refined by use and development, especially in British

Commonwealth nations and the United States. Court decisions have also played a large role in shaping U.S. trust law down to the finest of details, often with major legal and tax consequences.

Domestic Trusts

Decades ago the trust was promoted by U.S. investment advisers and lawyers (whose assistance has become essential for trust creation) as one of the best methods for people of wealth to both avoid creditor or other attacks and guarantee the future use they intend for their property after death. Unfortunately, for many U.S. investors and/or their heirs many of these trust-advocating financial advisors provided legally faulty trust plans and implementing documents later nullified by state or federal court decisions or U.S. Internal Revenue Service rulings beginning in the 1970's. In the U.S. there have been a host of bogus "trust experts" offering for sale supposedly fool proof trust arrangements which the courts subsequently ruled illegal or a transparent sham.

Depending on applicable national and local tax law, properly created trusts often can avoid inheritance taxes which diminish or destroy the value of property sought to be passed to the next generation. But the attorney you choose to create your trust must know U.S. federal and state trust and tax law thoroughly, or you and your heirs could not only lose money and assets but be tied up in legal and tax battles for years.

Trust Creation: It's Not Easy

The person who creates a trust, usually called the "grantor" or "settlor," conveys legal title to his property or money (the "corpus") to a third party (the "trustee"), perhaps a trusted friend, professional financial manager or a bank which has a trust department, to be managed or invested by the trustee for the benefit of a named person(s) or other "beneficiary." A document the grantor must sign describing the terms of the trust, called a "declaration" or "indenture" gives specific details of the manner in which the trust is to be administered and how its income is to be distributed, either or both during the grantor's life or afterward.

The Testamentary Trust

Trusts can be created while the grantor is living ("inter vivos") but the most common form is a "testamentary trust" included by a person in his last will, to take effect at death. This allows provision for loved ones, especially when the grantor has concern about the beneficiary's ability to manage his or her own affairs, i.e., the so-called "spendthrift trust" the assets of which are immune from creditor attacks.

While popular, testamentary trusts have distinct disadvantages often unexplained by legal advisors: estate and income taxes must be paid at the death of the grantor although successive estate tax levies often can be avoided as trust property passes to beneficiaries and their heirs in later years; testamentary trusts are subject to initial probate and sometimes to continuous court supervision which often entails great legal expense; all the activity of the testamentary trust and its trustee is a matter of public record and scrutiny.

In addition to trusts created in wills, trusts can be created formally ("express trusts") by contract, or, when real or personal property is involved, by a deed of trust. An "implied trust" may result in the absence of a formal trust when a court finds its creation from factual circumstances.

Under the law legal title and ownership to the trust corpus passes from the grantor to the trustees. Control of these assets is vested in the trustee(s) so long as the trust exists. The trust beneficiary receives only an equitable title to the income or property of the trust as limited under the terms of the trust declaration. Powers and duties of a trustee can be broad or narrow according to the declaration but should carefully reflect the grantor's intentions as to how the trust is to be used.

Living Trusts: Revocable and Irrevocable

A "living trust," in contrast to a testamentary trust, is created by the grantor to take effect and operate immediately while he or she is still alive. It avoids many of the liabilities of a testamentary trust.

A "revocable living trust" is a paper entity sanctioned by Anglo-American law to which a grantor can transfer his title to assets in any amount and of any kind, real, personal or mixed; money, insurance policies, a home, auto, boat, shares of stock, or ownership of a corporation. Usually there are several trustees named to manage the affairs of the transferred property which is held in the name of the trust. Because it is revocable, the grantor retains the power during his life to vary the trust terms, withdraw assets, or even end the trust by formal revocation. But upon the death of the grantor the trust which avoids probate immediately becomes irrevocable. Under its terms it is then administered by the trustees for the benefit of the named beneficiaries.

There are real benefits to a revocable living trust, the most obvious being the grantor's ability to manage the trust assets during his life and to end the trust whenever changed circumstances dictate. Other than his ability to arrange for the desired provision for family or others upon his death, the grantor receives no real immediate financial benefits from such a trust. But for a spouse or heirs as beneficiaries, there are many benefits in addition to acquiring income from trust assets. These advantages include: avoiding judicial probate with attendant expense and time delays (trust property is not included in the grantor's personal estate); allowing the uninterrupted operation of a family business placed in trust; avoiding public scrutiny of personal financial matters; causing no temporary stop in income for beneficiaries during probate after death; allowing the trust settlor a choice of the most advantageous law to govern the trust which can be created in any political jurisdiction.

Trust Tax Advantages

Under United States tax laws income and assets of a revocable or irrevocable trust are subject to state and federal death taxes. But such trusts can be arranged so that upon the subsequent deaths of named beneficiaries, or their heirs, further death taxes can be avoided, a real but often distant advantage for the trust beneficiaries. You should know that there exists a substantial body of American case law in which the I.R.S. has challenged successfully some trusts as being no more than evasive devices seeking to avoid tax liability.

The "Business Trust"

One type of trust which once was popular in the United States is the so-called "business trust." This hybrid legal device was designed to operate a business and have it produce a profit as compared to other conventional trusts which mainly sought asset protection and passive income. The business trust is an association of trustees who actively hold title to property and operated a business under the terms of a trust agreement for the benefit of shareholders who are the owners of the trust and share in profits. This arrangement is somewhat like a corporation but is easier to form since it requires only a signed agreement. Since this trust is entirely private it can avoid many government reporting requirements and conceal the actual owners.

Obviously this arrangement does little to provide asset protection and thus the complicated business trust bares little relationship to a Swiss annuity.

Trust Disadvantages

U.S. domestic trust law restricts the nature and extent of benefit and/or control that a settlor can retain after creating a trust. The law says when a settlor fails truly to place his former assets out of his own reach then those assets may not be out of reach of the settlor's creditors, past, present or future. This judicial doctrine has often been used, years later, when a court examines the way in which the trust property was actually handled, to upset even the best-intentioned trust plans.

In addition courts are hospitable to suits by creditors of the settlor who allege the trust was only a sham to avoid payment of just debts or judgments.

Trusts vs. Swiss Annuities

I have offered this detailed discussion of trusts because I believe Swiss insurance annuities can meet all the objectives and offer all the advantages of a trust while avoiding the known disadvantages including legal complexity and high creation costs.

Here is a detailed comparison of the domestic Anglo-American trusts and the Swiss annuity:

1) Income, Interest, and Dividends:

The financial productivity of a trust will depend on the nature of the assets placed in trust, the restrictions placed on trust management and the financial acumen and ability of the trustees. If it is a revocable or living trust, the settlor who creates the trust will probably be around for a time as one of the trustees; he retains partial management, the power of revocation and can change assets or trust provisions. If it is a testamentary trust the settlor is deceased and the beneficiaries can only hope the chosen trustee is a good financial manager. The creation of a trust does not guarantees any particular level of income. Trusts have thrived financially but they also have failed because of bad management or even illegal or dishonest acts by those in charge.

On the other hand, a contract for a Swiss insurance annuity is guaranteed by the insurance company to provide an income for life, interest and dividends, and depending upon its provisions, payment to beneficiaries upon the death of the insured. A second guarantee of the safety of the annuity and the issuing company exists because of annuity-favorable Swiss statutory law and its many safeguards. A third guarantee is the annuity's pay out in near-inflation proof Swiss francs convertible into any currency. Lastly there is the historic economic and political stability of Switzerland itself and especially of our insurance industry.

2) Reporting requirements:

A living trust generally need not be reported but many U.S. jurisdictions require some registration of trust creation. A testamentary trust, as part of a will, is subjected to probate court review and approval and as such comes under public scrutiny. If a trust is legally challenged by a party in interest or by the I.R.S. it can become the subject of prolonged court proceedings in the public spotlight.

A Swiss insurance annuity need not be reported to Swiss officials and all transactions of acquiring and maintaining an annuity are subject to strict Swiss bank secrecy laws. The fact of acquiring a foreign insurance annuity is reportable to the I.R.S. for purposes of a 1% excise tax but the annuity need not be described or registered in any way. The excise tax is like a sales tax, and is not part of your income tax return.

3) Exchange controls:

If a nation imposes currency, price or other economic controls an existing trust, either domestic or a foreign asset protection trust, and its income will undoubtedly be affected in myriad ways. A Swiss insurance annuity escapes such controls, unlike a foreign citizen's funds in a Swiss bank account which may be subjected to possible repatriation.

Although exchange controls are unlikely in the nations catering to asset protection trusts they could happen.

4) Protection from creditors:

Poorly created Anglo-American trusts often have been subjected to successful state and federal court attack by creditors or the I.R.S. alleging the device is simply a debt or tax avoidance mechanism. Using broad principles of common law U.S. courts have declared many trusts legal nullities based on a wide variety of technical grounds thus stripping the settlor and his assets of creditor protection. American courts have invalidated trusts, among other reasons, because there was insufficient independence on the part of trustees; the settlor retained actual control of the "irrevocable trust" assets or income; there was assignment of pre-tax personal services and related income to a trust; the trust was found to be a "sham devoid of economic reality," and; on the general grounds that the trust or its objectives were "against public policy" as in the case of the famous recent Girard trust in Pennsylvania. (After more than a century of operation and millions of dollars in grants the Girard trust provision providing educational scholarships to needy male students was found by a state court to be "against public policy" since it did not include help to needy females).

In recent years American courts have begun imposing added fines and penalties after taxes on those found guilty of attempting to create trusts for tax avoidance. Revocable trusts have proven especially vulnerable to attacks by determined creditors and often are treated by U.S. courts as additional assets of a debtor although such trust assets are more difficult to attach.

Compare the attitude of U.S. courts towards the trust with that of the official Swiss position regarding insurance.

The creation and existence of Swiss insurance annuities are sanctioned and governed by Swiss civil law which prevents annuities from being subjected to bankruptcy proceedings when the legal requirements are met. The law also prevents enforcement of foreign court judgments obtained by creditors or others when these same legal requirements are met. Swiss courts do not base their jurisprudence on vaguely elastic concepts like "public policy" but rather on clear statutory and case law.

In my opinion a Swiss annuity guarantees privacy and is virtually creditor proof.

5) Taxation:

Most trusts are subject to U.S. and state death taxes at the time of the settlor's passing although they can be drafted to avoid further death taxes when beneficiaries or later heirs die. U.S. income taxes are imposed on trust income, which is imputed to the settlor in revocable trusts, just as on any other ordinary income he might receive.

By comparison, American tax treatment of income from foreign insurance annuities is much more favorable. U.S. income taxes are imposed on only a small portion of life income from Swiss annuities, as we have seen, and accumulated earnings of annuity interest and dividends are not taxed by the U.S. Such annuities are exempt from all Swiss taxation.

6) Convenience:

The creation of a trust is a delicate and complex matter requiring expert legal and tax advice, often in more than one country, as we have seen. Because of highly technical provisions essential to proper trust creation, few layman have the ability to judge the end product but must take the word of their legal advisors. Similarly, trust administration must meet strict established legal and I.R.S. rules, regulations and reporting requirements or the trust may be subject to court attack and dissolution.

We already have discussed in detail the relatively simple creation of a Swiss annuity which is accomplished by the drafting of an insurance contract reflecting your personal wishes.

Termination is also an issue. While Anglo-American revocable trusts can be terminated at any time and testamentary trusts are revocable until the settlor's death, some other types of trusts are irrevocable regardless of changed circumstances.

Swiss annuities can be canceled at any time. After one year from creation of the annuity this can be done without loss of principal, interest or dividends.

Both trust assets, other than testamentary trusts, and Swiss annuities are exempt from probate as part of the settlor's estate.

7) Cost of Creation:

The creation and administrative cost of a trust can be huge, especially in the case of a testamentary trust which is challenged in court after the settlor's death or in the case of a foreign asset protection trust which will be examined in the next chapter.

There is no fee cost in purchasing a Swiss annuity other than the lump sum premium or later premium payments made prior to the start of deferred life income. All fees are paid by the insurance company and this administrative cost is equally figured into all annuity and other policy premiums.

Summary

All of the objectives of a domestic trust can be met more simply and conveniently by investing in a Swiss income annuity. The Swiss annuity also offers the tax and confidentiality advantages of having your assets in a foreign country, but a very reliable and investor-friendly one.

Reviewing the various trust mechanisms I have described you can easily discern the distinct investment advantages of a Swiss insurance annuity. The Swiss annuity is an uncomplicated, low cost means of producing a continuing guaranteed life income, assured death benefits to your chosen beneficiaries, as well as unquestioned protection of your assets from litigation, creditors and higher domestic taxes. And you do not need a lawyer to create a Swiss annuity.

International Asset Protection Trusts

Recently another asset protection device in trust form has gained popularity, the international asset protection trust ("APT"). This foreign trust often appears to be attractive to persons wishing to shield personal assets from possible law suits or other potential liability.

Protection Against the Unexpected

Medical, legal and professional malpractice suits as well as legislative and judicial imposition of no-fault personal liability on corporate officers and directors have by now become a fact of U.S. business life. An active business or professional person can suddenly be held responsible for all sorts of unforseen events such as a company's environmental pollution, a bank failure or a dissatisfied client. Premiums for malpractice insurance have gone through the roof. In this business climate astute people must consider the best way to protect their personal assets against any eventuality.

One way is to place those assets beyond the reach of potential litigation plaintiffs, creditors and their contingent-fee lawyers is creation of an asset protection trust located in a foreign country where the law favors such goals. Certain of these foreign jurisdictions do not recognize U.S. or any non-domestic court orders and a creditor must retry completely the original claim which gave rise to the U.S. judgment.

The country chosen for such a trust must have local trust experts who understand fully and are able to assist you in your objectives. The foreign local attorney who creates your trust unquestionably must know the applicable law and tax consequences or you will be in trouble from the start.

Once established the offshore asset protection trust in its basic form can consist of as little as a trust account in an international bank located in the foreign country. Many well established multi-national banks can provide trustees for such arrangements and are experienced in such matters. With today's instant communications and international banking facilities it is as convenient to hold assets and accounts overseas as it is in another American city. Most international banks offer U.S. dollar-denominated accounts which often offer better interest rates than U.S. institutions.

Pros and Cons

Because a foreign jurisdiction is the situs of such a trust, the cost of creating an asset protection trust abroad usually is more than $15,000 initially, plus several thousand dollars in annual maintenance fees. Usually unless the assets you seek to shield are worth more than $2 million such a trust may not be practical.

Business Week magazine estimates that "as a rule of thumb you should have a net worth of around $500,000" or more in order to justify a foreign asset protection trust, noting that some expert's fees for establishing and administering such trusts have run as high as $50,000 and some even ask a percentage of the assets to be transferred.

Depending on the country of choice, the settlor of a foreign asset protection trust can gain many advantages including the exercise of far greater control over assets and income from the trust than permitted under U.S. domestic law. Generally the U.S. rule which does not permit a settlor to create a trust for his own benefit does not apply in foreign countries. Creation of such a trust also means removal of your assets as a law suit target since domestic creditors are discouraged when faced with enforcement of a U.S. judgment in another country. However, the greater degree of control over the assets that the settlor maintains, the easier it is for a U.S. court, which has jurisdiction over the settlor, to order the settlor to return the assets to the jurisdiction of the court.

The trust can provide privacy, confidentiality, and reduced domestic reporting requirements in your own country; avoidance of domestic taxes and probate in case of death; increased flexibility in conducting affairs in case of disability, in transferring assets, international investing, or avoiding domestic currency controls. A foreign asset protection trust can also substitute for or supplement costly professional liability insurance or even a prenuptial agreement as protection for your heirs and their inheritance.

Trust Creation Abroad

The structure of foreign asset protection trusts is not very different than that of an Anglo-American trust. The settlor creates the trust and transfers the title to his assets to the trust to be administered according to the trust declaration by the trustees. Usually the trustee is a bank in the jurisdiction chosen. Beneficiaries can vary according to the settlor's estate planning objectives and the settlor may be a beneficiary but not the primary one.

Many foreign jurisdictions also permit appointment of a trust "protector" who, as the title indicates, oversees the operation of the trust to insure its objectives are being met and the law is followed. A protector does not manage the trust but can veto actions in some cases.

Under U.S. tax law foreign asset protection trusts are tax-neutral and are usually treated the same as domestic trusts, meaning income from the trust is treated as the settlor's personal income and taxed accordingly. Because the settlor retains some degree of control over the transfer of his assets to the foreign trust U.S. gift taxes can usually be avoided. (But that degree of control can make the settlor vulnerable to court orders requiring him to exercise that control, thus defeating the asset protection he intended to gain.) Estate taxes are imposed on the value of trust assets for the settlor's estate but all existing exemptions such as those for martial assets can be used. Asset protection trusts are not subject to the 35% U.S. excise tax imposed on transfers of property to a "foreign person."

As you will see in our discussion of partnerships in the next chapter, one device for a settlor to retain control of assets is to form a limited partnership and make the foreign asset protection trust a limited partner. This allows a general managing partner/settlor to retain control over all assets he transfers to the asset protection trust/limited partner abroad at the same time trust assets are theoretically protected from creditors or other legal attacks.

Some American court decisions recently have reduced the scope of asset protection of a limited partner, in cases holding that under certain circumstances assets can be attached by a judgment creditor, even though the people selling these programs often insist that the limited partnership is unassailable.

The greatest worry about a foreign asset protection trust often is the distance between you, your assets and the people who manage them. (While your assets do not have to be transferred physically to the foreign country in which the trust exists some circumstances may dictate such a precautionary transfer. Without such a transfer, a court could decide not to recognize the trust and take possession of the assets.) There is also the hassle of choosing people on whom you feel you can rely to create and assist you in managing the trust. Then there is high start up and annual running costs we mentioned.

If you are considering a foreign asset protection trust you should find out whether the foreign jurisdiction's laws are favorable, clear, and truly do offer the protection you seek. Examine the economic and political stability of the country, the reputation of its judicial system, local tax laws, the business climate, language barriers and available communication and financial facilities. Unfortunately there are very few U.S. experts in this field of asset protection law.

Several offshore financial centers have developed legislation hospitable to foreign-owned asset protection trusts, among them the Caribbean-area nations of the Cayman Islands, the Bahamas, Belize, the Turks and Caicos Islands, and the Cook Islands near New Zealand, as well as Cyprus and Gibraltar in the mediterranean.

Fair Weather Financial Planning

An important consideration about foreign asset protection trusts; this arrangement will only work if it is planned and created at a time of financial calm, not in a personal crisis. If the foreign trust is set up when you are about to be (or have been) sued or are forced into bankruptcy, the act of transferring your assets to a foreign trust is likely to run afoul of strict fraudulent conveyance laws in the U.S. which protect creditors. These laws allow a court to declare a trust or any device used to conceal or remove assets from creditors as illegal and therefore void. If your assets are still within the court's jurisdiction, your having conveyed title to a foreign trustee is not likely to protect them from domestic attachment in such a case. If the assets actually are in the foreign jurisdiction, as in a bank account, the creditor will have more difficulty in reaching them before you can act to protect them.

Some Advice

In deciding how much of a portfolio should go to each type of investment, it is best to ignore the existence of the personal residence or a personally owned business. These are not really investment assets, and serve a different purpose. They do not provide ready access to capital for either growth or emergency funds. To achieve a properly balanced portfolio, it is better to diversify based on only the liquid investments. Otherwise one can find that the picture has become unbalanced, by including a very large part of the wealth in a non-liquid position, and counting that as part of the diversification.

Swiss Annuities by Comparison

A Swiss annuity provides greater protection than a foreign asset protection trust without the high costs of creation and maintenance and the difficulties of foreign administration. The creditor-proof Swiss annuity also allows you to control the distribution of your assets to named beneficiaries while providing you with a guaranteed life income with reduced U.S. tax obligations. The beneficiary clause of your annuity can be drafted to include multiple- or contingent-beneficiaries, thus giving it the same kind of flexibility as a traditional trust.

The choice between the Swiss annuity and the foreign trust is a case of choosing lower cost simplicity or costly complexity to achieve approximately the same general objectives.

The Swiss laws which protect the owners of Swiss annuities and regulate our insurance companies were not written recently to create asset havens. Unlike some small countries, Swiss laws are not likely to change on a political whim or just to attract high flying international money.

Offshore Corporations

Yet another legal device advocated by some as the perfect repository for asset protection is the creation of a corporation in a foreign nation ("offshore corporation") which you as the instigator will control through various indirect means. The theory is that your corporate ownership will be concealed from the U.S. or other governments allowing you financial privacy. The offshore corporation can hold legal title to foreign mutual funds or other valuable assets outside the U.S. thus sheltering income and profits from American taxes. Business can be conducted through a designated nominee thus shielding your secret participation from the prying eyes of creditors or the U.S. government.

In theory this sounds grand, but there are many practical problems associated with an offshore corporation.

First of all, just as required in establishing any domestic U.S. corporation, the legal formalities have to be strictly adhered to when you incorporate abroad and the cost of setting up the company can be considerable. You will need foreign local legal counsel who knows the law and understands your asset protection objectives. Corporations anywhere are rule-bound creatures requiring separate books and records, meetings, minutes and corporate authorizing resolutions which make it less flexible than many other arrangements.

Then there are the problems presented by U.S. tax law and court decisions upholding those laws. There is a U.S. tax on unrealized gains and income and capital gains taxes on transfers to foreign corporations. If the offshore company can be characterized as a "foreign personal holding company" the U.S. shareholder's portion of undistributed earnings will be taxed currently to him as ordinary income. The same I.R.S. rule applies if the offshore entity qualifies as a "controlled foreign corporation" but additional taxes are imposed on gain derived from the sale of corporate assets. There is an established series of U.S. cases in which the courts have looked behind the offshore corporate veil and attributed "constructive ownership" to the U.S. taxpayer as an individual. Similar actual control findings have been based on a "chain of entities" linking the taxpayer to the corporation. The courts will look to who has substantive control as opposed to paper nominees who exercise nominal control. In addition there are various specific I.R.S. reporting requirements when an offshore corporation is created and when you serve as an officer, director or 10% or greater shareholder in a foreign personal holding company or offshore corporation of any kind. The U.S. Supreme Court has even ruled that a U.S. taxpayer can be held guilty of "falsifying a federal income tax return" by maintaining he did not have certain foreign holdings and that Fourth Amendment guarantees regarding searches and seizures do not apply to documents located abroad pertaining to a U.S. taxpayer's ownership of foreign interests. And any unreported foreign corporation ownership is automatically a felony if it is discovered. When U.S. courts have concluded offshore corporations are being used to conceal assets or avoid taxes they have levied additional penalties and interest and often imposed criminal convictions.

Offshore Corporation vs. Swiss Annuity

It is worth noting that in purchasing a Swiss annuity one can achieve with far greater ease all the goals allegedly met by an offshore corporation. An annuity provides an entity into which to place your assets, a guaranteed income, near complete secrecy that is fully legal, liquidity and flexibility, reduced taxes on income and its creation is a matter of your signature which does not require an outlay of legal or other start up fees.

Partnerships vs. Swiss Annuities

Another income producing-asset protection plan which has had some acceptance in the United States is the so-called "family limited partnership" which sounds appealing but is hardly without legal and tax problems. Recent U.S. court decisions have called into question some fundamental advantages of the family limited partnership including its greatest attraction, insulation of partnership property from an individual partner's personal creditors.

It is understandable that a legal arrangement built on family economic interests would be popular in the United States where much of the country's wealth is held in millions of family businesses. One estimate holds that family business accounts for more than half the gross domestic product and provides about half the nation's jobs. Oddly enough, only three out of ten family businesses survive into the second generation, one in ten last to the third generation and the average family enterprise lasts only about twenty-four years. Many of the reasons for the demise of individual family businesses are found in family dynamics and psychology which overlap problems of both family and business, either of which can be daunting on its own. Active family partnerships often mirror all these concerns and cease because of them.

Partnerships Defined

First we should consider some basic facts about partnerships in general.

A "partnership" as defined by the Uniform Partnership Act, a variation of which is applicable in most states of the U.S., is "an association of two or more persons to carry on as co-owners a business for profit." A partnership requires an agreement between two or more competent persons to place their cash, assets, labor and skills into a business and divide the profits and losses, usually in proportion to the degree of each of their ownerships. A partnership is recognized for most legal purposes including contracts, credit, bankruptcy, incurring debt, marshalling assets, and acquiring and transferring property but it does not pay tax.

General Partnerships

In a "general partnership," which is usually used for a commercial business purpose, each general partner shares equally in management and control. Each partner is also equally personally liable for partnership debts (after partnership assets are exhausted) to the full extent of their own personal wealth, this being the greatest general partnership disadvantage. This liability is one of the reasons that persons involved in partnership businesses often seek asset protection.

There are distinct advantages to being a partner in a general partnership. A general partner shares in all profits and since partnerships are not taxed as such, avoids the double taxation imposed on corporate dividends (corporate income tax plus individual income tax). A general partner can withdraw his full contribution without taxation. Along with other general partners he jointly manages and conducts the business with complete access to all books and financial information and can obtain joint credit with other partners.

As noted, each partner can be held personally liable for all partnership debts, even those which result from one partner's negligent or harmful acts. General partnerships often must be dissolved when one partner files personal bankruptcy or dies unless quick arrangements are made for a buy out of that partner's interest or unless the partnership agreement allows for such events. Usually a deceased's partner's partnership interest must go through probate. Even though a partnership is not a taxable entity it must file an annual tax return and when one party dies his interest is subject to estate and inheritance taxes.

General partnerships are often faced with the personal problems inherent in any joint ownership arrangement resulting from divorces, inheritance by non-members who may be undesirable as partners or the sudden death of a partner. As you can see from this discussion, general partnerships do not serve any really useful role in personal asset protection.

Limited Partnerships

Limited partnerships have been recognized in Anglo-American common law and in civil law for centuries. In a U.S. limited partnership the Uniform Limited Partnership Act requires there be one managing "general partner" (not to be confused with members of a general partnership as just described) who is solely responsible for management and control of the business. The limited partners must refrain from taking part in management lest in the eyes of the law they lose their limited status and its considerable benefits. The virtue of a limited partnership lies in the fact that limited partners are not individually liable for partnership debts beyond the property interest they contribute to the partnership.

Another advantage of a limited partnership is that a personal creditor of a limited partner cannot attach that partner's interest in the partnership. A creditor can only obtain what is known as a "charging order," a relatively unattractive remedy in the judgment collection process usually requiring the creditor to wait for the future distribution of partnership income, a totally discretionary act resting with the managing partner.

The courts of the State of California, which has one of the most liberal partnership laws, have recently called into question the near creditor-proof status of a limited partner and his partnership assets. In two cases these courts have held that under certain circumstances a debtor's partnership interest can be foreclosed to honor a judgment, a major departure from past holdings and a significant loss of asset protection. These decisions undermine the use of the family limited partnership for asset protection purposes, although many promoters sell family limited partnership packages which they claim are completely full proof asset protection devices.

"Family Partnerships"

The arrangement known as a "family partnership" is created as a means to transfer income and assets from the organizer or owner of a business or one who has accumulated assets of value to members of his or her family in a manner which limits personal and tax liability. It is nothing more than a regular limited partnership in which family members rather than non-family business associates are the partners. This arrangement comes with all the intra-family problems we noted as well as the advantages of close relationships.

Under the law in most states there is a requirement that a formal "articles of limited partnership" be signed and publicly registered with the state as notice of the business scope and the limits of partners' liability. These documents are technical, requiring legal and tax advice in order to insure both the partners' maximum advantage and that the agreement is valid.

The California cases cited may also have a future effect on the recent popularity of family partnerships as asset protection vehicles. The principal reason for laws providing partnership interest protection has been to prevent the creditors of one limited partner from disrupting partnership business continuity and harming the other partners by a foreclosure. If the only business of the partnership is the holding of family assets, including a personal residence, it may be difficult to argue that the family partnership has any real business in a commercial sense which will be disrupted by the foreclosure or that the business of innocent, non-related third parties will be prejudiced.

Family limited partnerships have been under legal siege in other important respects as well.

The U.S. Internal Revenue Service in a series of court cases, some appealed to the U.S. Supreme Court, has often successfully challenged the validity of both limited and family partnerships. In so doing the courts have imposed a series of tests which must be met in order to create a valid family (or any) limited partnership. In these tests the courts inquire into whether each partner (especially if a minor) has true title to and control of his or her interest; regardless of statements in the partnership articles, what is the true intent and relationship of the parties; what actual capital and/or skill does each partner contribute; and does each limited partner really control the income paid to him and its disposition?

These tests mean a family partnership, like any limited partnership, must have partners who actually perform important work on a continuing basis and who really contribute capital or assets of some tangible kind. The law does allow a limited partner to receive his or her partnership interest as a gift but if the recipient is a minor, someone other than the donor must serve as legal custodian of that interest until he or she reaches majority, 18-years-old in most states. A limited partner may also purchase his or her partnership interest with payment out of future profits. But there are restrictions on gift and purchased limited partnership interests, and most courts carefully scrutinize whether the donor actually relinquishes control and ownership of the interest and gives it over to the donee or purchaser.

As compared to a general partnership, if it is properly created and managed, a limited partnership can be a valid asset protection arrangement in some circumstances. Although a partnership is usually thought of as operating a commercial business enterprise it can also be used to control personal assets such as a home or other real estate, personal property and intangibles such as stocks, bonds and even insurance. A family limited partnership can also be the owner of a Swiss annuity.

If a large amount of money is involved it is better to create more than one limited partnership, one of which holds liquid assets such as cash, securities, bonds, certificates of deposit, precious metals, life insurance policies and negotiable instruments. The other could include assets such as real estate and business assets which might be more vulnerable to creditor attack.

The managing general partner retains control over all the limited partnership assets and the limited partners who may be family members cannot and must not assert any power in management. With the caveat expressed above concerning new court holdings, family partnership assets are generally safe from personal creditors of the limited partners and in turn the limited partnership's creditors can only attack a limited partner to the extent of that partner's actual investment and then only with extreme difficulty and usually little result. For example, a partnership can accumulate assets but cannot be compelled to distribute them to partners thus protecting both the assets and the partner from a creditor's charging order.

If a parent serves as a managing general partner with a small ownership interest (say 5%) and his children or spouse serve as limited partners with most of the ownership divided among them (95%), when the managing partner/parent dies, inheritance and estate taxes are limited to the deceased's actual partnership interest which can be a considerable saving for the heirs/limited partners. There is no bar to managing partner contributing the majority of the limited partnership's assets and receiving only a small percentage ownership interest which gives his creditors little to pursue. Similarly when income is distributed in a limited partnership it does not have to be in proportion to a partner's investment or degree of ownership; it can be in any proportion and family members can be given a disproportionately large share. Whatever the income distribution may be, each partner is liable for U.S. income taxes as ordinary income.

Keep in mind also that any legal entity can be a general or limited partner, a domestic or foreign trust, a corporation, estate, custodian of a minor or an association. This means that a managing general partner in a limited partnership can incorporate for that management purpose, further providing protection for his corporate self from creditors and possibly higher taxes. The corporate general partner might have a fraction of a percent of ownership interest, but provides another layer of insulation from suits for acts of the partnership.

From the foregoing you can properly conclude that a family limited partnership has the potential of being an excellent vehicle for sheltering both personal and family assets from creditors and for reducing estate and inheritance taxes. But these partnerships come at a price. Unless carefully crafted by expensive legal experts, American courts are far too eager to use legal loopholes to overturn an alleged "partnership." Even more important than the legal crafting of the initial documents is the importance that the day-to-day partnership operations conform precisely to the legal requirements. Substance is at least as important as form, a detail that many family partnership package promoters and their clients overlook. After the fact a family may find itself in a situation worse than if nothing been done.

While there is a certain flexibility in a family partnership for the managing general partner, the donor still must deed absolutely his assets to the partnership and normally all partners must agree before partnership assets can be sold or transferred. As with any partnership, unless the partnership agreement and relevant state statutues specifically provide otherwise, one partner's death or bankruptcy may force the dissolution of the partnership (or a forced buy out) at an inopportune time for the sale and distribution of assets. Remember partnership assets are taxed fully as part of a deceased partner's estate. Undistributed income may place a partner in a significantly higher personal income tax bracket at an unexpected time, since partners are taxed on their share whether or not the income is distributed.

The value of a family partnership, like any investment comes from good management and wise decisions. Forming a family partnership does not guarantee income or benefits, nor even asset protection. Ultimately any value for you or your heirs will rest not only on a particular legal device but on the strength of the national currency in which its benefits are paid.

Family limited partnership compared to the Swiss Annuity

Contrast the family limited partnership with a Swiss annuity and you see a limited partnership lacks many of the benefits of the annuity. A Swiss annuity is guaranteed to provide you with life payments of competitive dividends and interest with minimal governmental reporting requirements. You don't need lawyers to create it, nor accountants to file special business tax returns for the partnership and each partner each year. Funds invested in an annuity are protected from government repatriation or control. A Swiss annuity can provide instant liquidity and is subject to no Swiss taxes and greatly reduced U.S. income taxes. Most importantly, an annuity gives uncomplicated convenience in creation, operation and cancellation. The purchaser of an annuity decides its terms; it is not something debated at a family conference.

A Swiss annuity plugs the loopholes inherent in a family limited partnership while still allowing multiple contingent beneficiaries and does all this with a substantial tax saving.

Lastly, annuities are sanctioned by Swiss federal law and overseen by government agencies. Swiss law permits the creation of the insurance company, authorizes the issuance of the annuity by the company, protects by regulation and supervision the manner in which the company administers the annuity and makes its investments and protects your annuity from court judgments.

Contrast these guarantees written into Swiss law with the many U.S. court decisions in which family and other limited partnerships have been overturned on technical or "public policy" grounds after attack by a disgruntled family member, a creditor or the I.R.S.

We think it reasonable to conclude that a family partnership properly created and managed may be a good asset protection strategy but a better, safer method is found in the Swiss annuity.

Swiss Annuities vs. U.S. Annuities

More on the U.S. Insurance Industry

We previously considered the fact that over 400 American insurance companies have failed in the last two decades. If you are a U.S. citizen thinking of purchasing a domestic annuity the financial reliability of the insurance company you pick must be an important factor in making your decision.

Too few people in the United States, or the world financial community, seem to realize that even greater American insurance scandals might erupt. State auditors in 1992 conducted an astonishing and virtually unreported study of the U.S. insurance regulatory system suggesting the potential for just such a massive scandal perhaps far worse in impact and scope than the savings and loan debacle. Indeed, the study reads like an outline for a best-selling crime novel with insurance executives and state regulators as villains.

With great pain much of American business over the last decade has reformed and modernized itself (or been forced to change by government regulators or the demands of mergers and acquisitions). Most banks, securities firms, and financial companies are managed quite differently (and usually better) than a decade or so ago. It may take a crisis such as the savings and loan scandal to force U.S. insurance companies to adopt modern management and truly safe investment practices.

State Auditors Report

In one of the most sweeping and damning indictments of state insurance regulation yet issued, the state auditors of eleven major states in the joint study found U.S. insurance companies are riddled with mismanagement, fraud, deception, and uncertain finances. They found it common practice for state insurance regulators to take years to discover problems and years more to do anything about them.

The study found disturbing parallels with the early stages of the savings and loan collapse, including inadequate industry reporting, varying and often conflicting regulation and enforcement, rapid growth, expansion into new and unrelated lines of business, mismanagement and fraud, excessive risk taking with investments in junk bonds and commercial real estate, improper dealings with affiliated entities and poor internal controls. (Contrast that gloomy official picture with the solid Swiss insurance industry).

The auditors' study was a joint performance audit of their state insurance commission colleagues designed to evaluate the adequacy of the current state regulatory system. In spite of the dire nature, these conclusions were greeted with relative silence at the White House and on Capitol Hill (as were the first signs of the savings and loan scandal a decade ago).

The auditors concluded that multi-state regulatory control prevented any effective national oversight of the insurance industry. With fifty state regulatory bodies in charge they concluded no one is really in charge. The reason, they found, was mainly that state regulators fail to take timely or concerted appropriate action when a problem insurer is identified. Just such a factor led the savings and loan crisis to explode in the 1980's. The auditors also found the National Association of Insurance Commissioners (NAIC) does not adequately coordinate regulatory information and activities among the states. In this lax regulatory environment troubled insurers are able to operate for extended periods, often years, without being forced to resolve their problems.

The report cites a horror list of industry malpractice and regulatory sloth and inattention. A few examples:

- The auditors studied sixteen insurer insolvencies between 1985 and 1991. In most, regulators knew the insurer was in trouble at least five, sometimes ten years before they took action (and then it was so late the insurers went bankrupt).
- Most state insurance departments do not rate an insurer's financial condition or share such information with regulators in other states.
- Some insurance departments do not even have guidelines for routine audit examinations, which means insurer data is not always compared with regulatory standard NAIC financial ratios or audited financial reports. Loss reserves are not reviewed and reported and investment values are not verified.
- There have been many abuses involving holding companies and affiliates, including inter-company sham transactions, assets being drained from subsidiaries, improper loans, shifting devalued

junk bonds to unreported affiliates, swapping good assets for worthless assets and improper reinsurance.

- State regulators do not oversee insurance holding companies and often have no power to regulate the parent's non-insurance affiliates. Currently, only thirteen states require consolidated financial statements of multi-faceted insurers.

The state auditors concluded that insurance regulators should focus efforts on identifying problem companies and taking prompt action. They also called for some mechanism to reduce the impact of insurance company failures and improve the process for protecting insured persons victimized by failed companies.

In 1993 two of the major U.S. insurance companies, the securities divisions of Prudential and Metropolitan Life, were exposed as fraudulently enticing thousands of clients with false claims representing life insurance as retirement investment plans and defrauding limited partnership investors. Both companies are now exposed to millions of dollars of claims from those who were harmed.

If all this sounds serious, that's because it is. And yet this shaky atmosphere reflects the true state of the U.S. insurance industry and many individual companies which issue and guarantee annuities.

"Lump it or Leave It"

The possibility of purchasing an annuity typically arises in the United States at the time a person retires from lengthy employment and becomes eligible for some form of company pension payments. At retirement the issue is often "lump it or leave it" since the retiree's choice may be to leave his or her funds with the company pension plan and receive a lifetime of monthly payments or to take out the accumulated lump sum and invest it in some more secure or profitable payment plan, often an annuity.

Is Your Pension Secure?

One very important factor to be considered in whether you take out a lump sum payment at your retirement is the financial soundness of the company upon which you expect to depend for your life long pension payments. Many of the largest U.S. companies have been skimping on their employee pension fund contributions for decades creating a large gap between promised benefits and assets from which to satisfy these obligations to retired workers. More than 65,000 pension plans in theory are covered by federal insurance but no one pretends a general pension collapse could be paid for by a government already bailing out the savings and loan industry, a government with unfunded obligations for its own employees' pensions amounting to many billions of dollars.

The official U.S. government agency, the Pension Benefit Guarantee Corporation, which "insures" pension plans, recently published its list of the fifty companies with the most poorly funded pension plans. The combined shortfall rose by more than 30% during 1993 to $38 billion, up from $14.2 billion in 1992. General Motors alone admits to having $24 billion in unfunded pension liability and is trying to issue stock to finance this deficit (which would not be worth much if GM goes under).

All this should prompt you to give serious examination to your own employer's financial security. The safest course may be for you to take your lump sum and invest it elsewhere.

For people with enough sophistication to choose and carefully watch their investments or those with expert and trustworthy financial advisors, taking the lump sum may be the best way to go. As long as pension money is transferred directly ("rolled over") into an individual retirement account (IRA) it escapes the 20% withholding tax imposed on straight withdrawals. If you later need money you can cash in some of your investments, paying ordinary income tax rates (the top marginal rate is now 39.6%) on only what is taken out. It is worth noting that the Pension Benefit Guarantee Corporation sets the interest rate you will be paid on lump sum pension payments which in 1993 was 4.25% for $25,000 or less and 5.1% for amounts above $25,000, much below Swiss annuity interest rates when combined with favorable Swiss franc convertability compared to the U.S. dollar.

Many people find it a nightmare to be forced to choose the right investments which will guarantee a life time income for them and their spouse. They don't want to be their own pension manager and actuarial expert.

The alternative is often an annuity which guarantees a periodic payment over a set period of time or for life. Many company pension plans, so-called "401K" accounts, and profit-sharing plans allow the choice of an annuity at retirement. Direct transfers of such funds can be made directly by your company to the insurer issuing the annuity, thus avoiding the 20% tax. The same transfer can be made directly to a Swiss insurance company when purchasing an annuity.

Unlike Switzerland, where the pay out rates differ little for most insurance companies, the amount you will be paid back in life income per $1,000 you invest in a domestic U.S. annuities will vary widely among insurance companies. In late 1993 Annuity and Life Insurance Shopper, which publishes comparative prices for immediate annuities for fifty insurance companies, found monthly payments ranging from $5.48 to $8.05 per $1,000 for a 50% joint and survivor annuity for a 65-year-old man and his 60-year-old wife. For a couple investing $100,000 in an annuity the best paying annuity would pay $257 per month more than the lowest paying plan. Prices vary because companies use different mortality assumptions and have different management expenses. This means that careful annuity shopping can produce 20% to 25% more in life income if you have the time and expertise to find the right company. But this higher yield is almost always a sign of higher risk.

Given the lax and contradictory state regulatory policies governing American insurance companies in the absence of federal regulation, and the multiple company failures in recent years, it makes sense to look for safety if an annuity is your retirement choice. Switzerland can offer near absolute safety. Objective observers realize the United States cannot.

Added to the recognized perilous state of the American insurance industry, the most telling argument against purchasing a U.S. domestic annuity payable in dollars has already been underscored in my discussion of the stability of the Swiss franc; avoiding U.S. economic instability and unfavorable inflation which erodes income value over time. Unlike U.S. Social Security benefits, there is no automatic annual increase in private annuity income to take inflation into account.

Iron-Clad Protection for Your Swiss Annuity Assets

Expanding your wealth is important, but so is protecting it from false claimants, and Switzerland excels in providing you such protection. As we have already previously discussed, anybody with wealth in the U.S. is a possible target for litigation and unjustified claims. With all the possible ways assets can be snatched from you, it is comforting to know there is a place where your property is safe and out of reach of everyone else.

According to Swiss law, insurance policies, including annuity contracts, cannot be seized by creditors. They also cannot be included in a Swiss bankruptcy procedure. Even if an American or other foreign court expressly orders the seizure of a Swiss annuity account or its inclusion in a bankruptcy estate, the court order will not be honored by Swiss authorities, provided that the annuity account has been structured the proper way.

To have this legal protection there are two requirements which must be part of the annuity contract: A U.S. resident who buys a life insurance policy from a Swiss insurance company must designate his or her spouse or descendants, or a third party (if done so irrevocably) as beneficiaries. Secondly, to avoid suspicion of making a fraudulent conveyance to avoid a specific judgment, under Swiss law, the person must have purchased the policy or designated the beneficiaries not less than six months before any bankruptcy decree or collection process began.

The policyholder can also protect the annuity by converting a designation of spouse or children into an irrevocable designation when he becomes aware of the fact that his creditors will seize his assets and that a court might compel him to repatriate the funds in the insurance policy. If the policyholder is subsequently ordered by a non-Swiss court to revoke the irrevocable designation of the beneficiary and to liquidate the policy he will not be able to do so since by law a Swiss insurance company cannot accept an instruction to change the designation of beneficiaries which is irrevocable.

Article 81 of the Swiss insurance statute provides that if a policyholder has made a revocable designation of spouse or children as beneficiaries, they automatically become policyholders and acquire all rights if the policyholder is declared bankrupt. In such a case the original policyholder therefore automatically loses control over the policy and also his right to demand the liquidation of the policy and the repatriation of funds. A foreign court therefore cannot compel the policyholder to do so. If the spouse or children notify the insurance company of the bankruptcy, the insurance company will note that in its records. Even if the original policyholder subsequently sends instructions because a court has ordered him to do so, the insurance company will ignore them. It is important that the company be notified promptly of the bankruptcy, so that they do not inadvertently follow the original policyholder's instructions because of lack of notice of the bankruptcy.

If the policyholder has designated his spouse or his children as beneficiaries of the insurance policy, the insurance policy is protected from his creditors regardless of whether the designation is revocable or irrevocable. The policyholder may therefore designate his spouse or children as beneficiaries on a revocable basis and revoke this designation before the policy expires if at such time there is no threat from any creditors.

Although I have gone to some length to reiterate the extreme legal protections provided by Swiss laws for your assets placed in annuities, I know you can appreciate the need for and comfort provided by such strict safeguards.

Additionally you should know that Swiss annuities under U.S. law can be a part of your Keogh Plan, IRA, or domestic corporate pension plan or can be used for the roll over option in your existing plan. In such event a U.S. trustee such as a bank can hold the annuity contract, thus meeting the U.S. legal requirement that the asset be physically held in the U.S.

Portfolio Bonds for Asset Protection

The most popular way of investing funds offshore is still the opening of a managed or unmanaged bank account with a bank located in a favorable offshore jurisdiction. In general, this is done either by directly purchasing individual shares with the bank, or through an offshore trust.

Rather unfamiliar to many offshore investors is an investment structure called Offshore Portfolio Bond (also known as Private Portfolio Bond, Offshore Insurance Bond, and others).

This investment vehicle combines the best of two worlds - banks and insurances: It is a professionally managed offshore bank account with the benefits of both, a traditional offshore trust and an offshore insurance investment.

The Portfolio Bond can be considered as a simple holding structure. Usually it's domiciled in an offshore tax haven, through which the investor (or his/her selected bank or adviser) can direct the insurance company to invest in a wide range of investment vehicles such as shares, unit trusts, cash deposits, bonds etc.

How it works

The investor closes a contract in his name with an offshore insurance company. He selects a bank and transfers the money to the insurance company's account at that bank. He receives a policy from the insurance company.

Legally the investor is the client of the insurance company and the insurance company is the client of the bank. As the insurance company's client the investor can keep full control of his assets.

According to his instructions, the money will be managed by the bank, an investment manager of his choice (such as Weber, Hartmann, Vrijhof & Partners discussed in the *Why Invest Abroad?* chapter) or by himself. In fact, an Offshore Portfolio Bond is a life insurance or an annuity policy. Its value consists precisely in the assets placed there by the life insurance company on the investor's behalf. The money now grows as managed.

Overview of benefits

Besides the important benefits of an offshore account with a private bank (confidentiality, individual asset allocation and strategy, personal care) a Portfolio Bond provides substantial additional benefits.

Separate estate planning

A Portfolio Bond allows to make distributions separate from your ordinary estate and to designate as beneficiary whoever you may wish. However, depending on the policy owner's home jurisdiction some compulsory portions of legal heirs might be reserved.

Upon your death the insurance company will transfer the money to the beneficiaries within 5 days after receipt of the death certificate.

No power of attorney, no last will and no certificate of inheritance are required. Your beneficiaries get immediate access to the money and it will be paid out according to your wish (e.g. lump sum or annual payments).

Asset Protection

Properly structured and established in the right jurisdictions, Portfolio Bonds enjoy legal protection from creditors and cannot be seized or be included in any bankruptcy proceeding. The asset protection comes from the insurance part in your Portfolio Bond.

In some jurisdictions the law is very strict and the protection rock solid. If properly structured, your money is protected even if there is a judgment or court order against you. This major advantage is of particular interest to professionals, or anyone who is exposed to possible lawsuits, malpractice cases, nervous creditors or vengeful ex-spouses.

Confidentiality and privacy

In some jurisdictions, an offshore Portfolio Bond is not just secret and discreet, but protected by law. In Liechtenstein, for example, there is an insurance secrecy law analogous to the banking secrecy law in Switzerland.

Furthermore, offshore insurance companies are strictly confidential and communicate exclusively with the owner of the policy. No information is provided to any third party (natural person or legal entity).

Tax advantages

Unlike many other offshore investments, Portfolio Bonds are, in some jurisdictions, completely free of local taxes. No taxes are due if purchased in offshore jurisdictions like Switzerland or Liechtenstein.

As far as income, capital gains and estate tax are concerned, the law of the investor's tax domicile is decisive.

In various countries insurance policies enjoy substantial tax benefits if correctly structured. Portfolio Bonds offer utmost flexibility and can be tailor-made to fit the legal requirements for tax privilege.

Insurance coverage

Depending on your needs and requirements for your heirs you can add insurance coverage to your portfolio in the event of your death. The amount of insurance can be chosen from zero up to whatever your requirements are and it can also be adjusted during the term of the contract.

This can be very important if a remaining spouse is forced to pay off a mortgage or if heirs need cash to buy out business partners.

Questions & Answers

What type of assets can be included in a Portfolio Bond?

The underlying investments can be freely selected. The portfolio can contain any investment of the investor's choice as long as the value can be established (e.g. non listed stock, real estate and shares of the client's own company etc.).

Can I pledge my Portfolio Bond?

Yes, but pledging your bond means you give up the benefit of asset protection.

Can I take a loan against my Portfolio Bond?

Yes, but the insurance company does not give a loan against a Portfolio Bond. The loan must come from the bank.

How safe is my portfolio if...

... the bank fails?

In some countries your portfolio is segregated from the bank's assets and therefore absolutely safe. In the event of bankruptcy of the bank, the insurance company - as the legal client of the bank - would, therefore, receive the portfolio back.

... the insurance company fails?

Some offshore jurisdictions have the world's strongest and strictest insurance industry laws. In Switzerland, for example, not once in the history of Swiss insurance has a company failed to meet its obligations or declared bankruptcy.

The financial safety of the insurance company is carefully supervised by the governmental insurance authorities. The law requires substantial reserves for each policy and the building of such reserves is carefully monitored by the auditors and the government.

How liquid is my Portfolio Bond?

In general the Portfolio Bond provides utmost liquidity. Money can be added and taken out with a few days notice.

If you have chosen a tax privileged solution, it might well be that your domestic tax law requires the funds to remain within the Portfolio Bond for a certain period or up to a certain age. However, if you need cash you can always borrow against your Portfolio Bond.

How do I receive information on my account?

You will receive quarterly statements through the insurance company. However, if you prefer not to receive any mail, a special mailing address in Switzerland or elsewhere can be used.

Can the insurance company change the bank?

Not without you instructing them to do so. As the owner of the Portfolio Bond you choose the bank and asset manager. Changes can only be made on your order.

Is a Portfolio Bond compatible with a trust?

Yes. Assigning your investments to an offshore trust is much cheaper and easier if they are grouped together under one bond, as this greatly simplifies the tax treatment of the structure and avoids the need to set up a specialized trust for which the running costs will be far greater.

How do I purchase a Portfolio Bond?

An application form needs to be completed together with a special instruction form (choice of bank, nature of funds, choice of manager) and handed over to the insurance company. The insurance company then opens an account at the bank of to the insurance company's account.your choice and you transfer the funds (money or stocks and bonds) directly.

The portfolio bond requires a minimum of around Swiss francs 200,000. If this is an appropriate investment for you, the experts to contact are:

NMG International Financial Services Ltd.
Goethestrasse 22, Suite 5
CH-8001 Zurich
Switzerland
Telephone +41-1-266 21 41
Fax +41-1-266 21 49 Please mark fax "Attn: Suite 5"

or by completing the Internet inquiry form at http://www.swissinvesting.com/nmg/

To Serve You in Switzerland

So you have decided to take the international plunge and place some of your investments in the safety of Switzerland. You can start on your own but it will be much easier if you have an experienced friend in Switzerland who knows the financial scene and is ready and willing to assist you.

The most practical way for foreign citizens to get information on Swiss annuities is to contact a Swiss insurance broker specializing in foreign business. This is because very few transactions are concluded directly by foreigners either with a Swiss insurance company or with regular Swiss insurance agents. The insurance agents and companies can legally handle the business directly but it isn't customarily done that way.

Permit me to suggest that the experienced friend you need can be found in NMG-IFS International Financial Services, providing independent professional financial services.. The NMG Group was originally formed as an actuarial consulting and related financial services company in Singapore in 1991. Today, NMG has become the largest provider of financial services consulting in Asia, and has established itself as a market leader in specialist advice on emerging economies. NMG now has consulting operations and representation in 18 citieson six continents.

NMG International Financial Services Ltd. is a subsidiary of the NMG Group domiciled in Zurich, Switzerland. It is an independent investment consultancy firm established to satisfy the investment and financial protection needs of international clients. We do this by selecting outstanding Swiss and international insurance and banking products while offering exceptional advice and service.

Their services include:

- Asset Protection Strategies
- Fixed, Variable, or Private Annuities and Endowments
- Portfolio Bonds
- Life insurance
- Bank Accounts
- World Class Portfolio Managers

Their investment solutions take in account global investment theories and strategies and individual and local investment requirements including tax advantages, asset protection and estate planning. Their worldwide network, experience and know-how enable them to select first class investment solutions through insurance companies, banks and international law firms and to

combine them to form one perfectly fitting solution.

As a one-stop source they take care of everything for you. They provide full sales and after sales services and deal on your behalf with banks, insurance companies and other service providers all over the world.

More information may be obtained from:

NMG International Financial Services Ltd.
Goethestrasse 22, Suite 5
CH-8001 Zurich
Switzerland
Telephone +41-1-266 21 41
Fax +41-1-266 21 49 Please mark fax "Attn: Suite 5"

or by completing the Internet inquiry form at http://www.swissinvesting.com/nmg/

About the Author

The editorial staff of SwissInvesting.com has compiled this material from many sources and famous financial authors, including Adam Starchild, Michael Checkan, Robert Vrijhof and Marc Sola. As the editors have merged this material into one document, it has not been possible to attach source credits to the individual paragraphs or sections.

Printed in the United States
86002LV00002B/77/A

keeping it real

ANNIE DALTON

HarperCollins *Children's Books*

This book is for Matt who was patient and clever, Claire for her sensitive comments, Andrea who kept me well-fed, and for all you undercover angels everywhere.

First published in Great Britain by HarperCollins *Children's Books* in 2005

HarperCollins *Children's Books* is a division of HarperCollins*Publishers* Ltd,
77–85 Fulham Palace Road, Hammersmith,
London, W6 8JB

The HarperCollins *Children's Books* website address is:
www.harpercollinschildrensbooks.co.uk

1

ISBN 0 00 716139 5

Printed and bound in England by
Clays Ltd, St Ives plc

Chapter One

I'd hate to shock any true angel believers out there, but before I died and became one myself, I didn't really believe in angels at all!

I don't blame myself *too* much for that. It's a natural mistake to make, if you grow up in a part of London where they put security guards *inside* Santa's Grotto to stop all the dads and big bros pinching the toys.

In my neighbourhood, if you couldn't break it, kick it, spray graffiti on it or nick it, it probably didn't exist.

If I HAD believed in angels, though, I'd have told you they *definitely* had everything sussed.

This belief has caused me SOO much trouble.

I made so many major bloopers when I first got here that even thinking about them still makes me cringe... However I couldn't exactly go back to being human, so I decided to just wing it. I winged my way so brilliantly through those first terms at the Angel Academy, you have no idea.

I took weekend courses in *très* deep subjects like soul retrieval. I picked up a LOT of fancy angel jargon. No, honestly, if you'd seen me sitting with my angel buddies at our fave table in Guru, nodding knowledgeably as they chatted about Dark Studies, I totally blended in!

During waking hours that is. Don't know if you've tried, but you can't actually *fake* it in your sleep.

I only had to lie down and close my eyes, and I'd instantly go slap-bang into a terrifying nightmare. Like all bad dreams, the plots were kind of samey. Usually I was trying to rescue my little sister from hideous evil beings who'd taken over my planet since I'd been dead.

When I wasn't dreaming about my family, I dreamed about my human mates. In dream after dream they angrily turned their backs on me. Especially Sky. She just could *not* understand why I'd had to leave.

I couldn't understand it either. I'd go to stare out at the twinkling lights of the Heavenly City and think, *Why me*? Did some sharp-eyed Agency scout go through Park Hall Community High School with a clipboard, awarding angel points? "Nope, nope, nope. Wait! That girl at the back! Not her – the one touching up her nail polish, let's take her!"

I can't imagine *anyone* looking at the Park Hall Mel Beeby and seeing potential angel material. Yet I scored an Agency scholarship to the coolest school in the cosmos and my mates got left behind.

Here's how it happened; you know, how I died.

It was the day after my thirteenth birthday: a bright, summery, completely happy day. I had a wodge of birthday cash in my purse and I was off to meet my mates for a BIG shopping splurge.

I glanced both ways, like you do, and stepped on to the pedestrian crossing as an ancient Ford Fiesta screeched round the corner, burning rubber. It was the last thing I saw: rusty metal and a white-faced boy gripping the wheel.

BANG!! The Universe went supernaturally quiet.

For a long moment nothing whatsoever happened. Then, to my surprise, I just stepped out of my body. It was as effortless as a pea slipping out of its pod.

Next minute I was soaring over the city; and I just kept on soaring higher and higher, until I soared right out of the solar system!

Strange as it seems now, the idea of turning back never occurred to me. It might have had something to do with the music: sweet throbbing chords which sounded as if they came from some giant humming top. I couldn't help myself – I started flying faster and faster, with a growing sense of excitement. I remember having a childish thought that when the music stopped my cosmic mystery tour would be over. But when I reached the light fields where Heaven begins, the music didn't stop; it just faded, weaving its otherworldly harmonies into the everyday hum of Heaven. And this was only the beginning of the cosmic mysteries...

Like, what are the chances of meeting your true soul-mate on your first day at angel school? Imagine two girls from two totally different centuries meeting outside the shimmery, mother-of-pearl gates at the Angel Academy and instantly recognising each other. Doesn't that just give you goose bumps?

You know the first thing Lola Sanchez said to me? "*Do I know you?*" That's what it's like when you meet your soul-mate.

Don't get the idea soul-mates are like, an exclusive angel phenomenon. People run into soul-mates on Earth too, you know. But there's a *leetle* complication known as the Powers of Darkness.

The PODS would SO prefer you *not* to hook up with your soul-mates. They'd prefer you not to have any friends full stop. Ideally, they want you to feel you can't trust *anyone, EVER*, starting with yourself. It's hard to recognise a soul-mate if you don't feel good inside your own skin. It's also harder to *be* a soul-mate.

Don't get me wrong, my human mates and I totally looked out for each other. At times Sky and I were so close we were more like sisters than friends. But we always had to keep that *leetle* tiny something back, or at least Sky did; like, deep down, she didn't actually trust you.

But Lola and I had total trust between us from the start. All friendships, even heavenly friendships, have ups and downs, but when you trust someone, you get through it, right?

Considering my soul-mate comes from a vibey city a hundred years in my future, it's unbelievable how much we have in common. We literally chat non-stop about anything that jumps into our heads, from purely frivolous stuff like, should we just give in to fashion and get those quite sweet forehead jewels (like a few of the older angel girls are wearing again at school), or is that TOO totally angel for words, to HUGE cosmic topics like Space and Time.

I have NEVER been able to get my head around the concept of *two* kinds of time. I'm sorry but to me 'Time' means the system I learned in primary school, which we do use in Heaven mostly. But apparently there's also Cosmic Time – like, the Boss of time – which can just kick in, totally overruling the first kind, if, but only *if,* the Universe decides...

I have a personal reason for telling you all this. I must have been at the Angel Academy for well over a year when it finally dawned on me that I hadn't had a birthday!

I know! I'd attended other kids' celebrations. I *organised* Lola's. Yet it never seemed to be my turn.

I tried bringing this up with my friends, but you'd think I was spying for the Dark Powers the way everyone fobbed me off. They reckoned it was something I had to discover for myself.

This is one of the things about angelic life that makes me want to *scream*. Everything has to be a

Big Mystery! What if I *didn't* discover it for myself? Was I supposed to stay thirteen for ever?

One night, I was watering my baby orange tree, in a real grump, when for no reason a touching human memory flitted into my head.

It was my little sister's fourth birthday. All afternoon, Jade and her pre-school playmates charged around our flat leaving a trail of torn wrapping paper and burst balloons. Finally the littlies went home clutching goody bags. When I went into Jade's room later, to say goodnight, she was dreamily staring out of the window into the dark. "What's up, Fluffyhead?" I teased.

My sister turned with an awed expression. "Mel, the moon is *smiling*," she breathed. "It *knows* it's my birthday!"

I knew what she meant. On your birthday you don't just feel special to your friends and family, you feel special to the entire Universe. It was this memory that finally pushed me over the edge. So what if I hadn't solved the Big Mystery? This angel's birthday was *seriously* overdue!!

I reached for my diary and flipped it open. Picking a Friday at random, I daringly circled it in sparkly felt-tip. Sorted!

I ran to Lola's room to tell her I was having a birthday party at Rainbow Cove, which was the first venue to pop into my head.

"Yayy!" she cheered to my surprise. "An excuse to go shopping!"

I spent the evening on the phone inviting everyone I could think of. They all went "OK, cool!" Our buddy Reuben said he and Chase would organise the music and lighting. Finally I phoned Mo, who runs Guru, our fave student hangout, and asked if he'd take care of catering. He said he'd be delighted!

I'd have given myself a b-day party months ago, if I'd known it was going to be this easy. Suspiciously easy is what it was.

Maybe it's just me and birthdays? Something cosmic always seems to happen on or around mine. But I never imagined that my first heavenly birthday would make all my terrifying nightmares come true.

Chapter Two

The Saturday before my official birthday, Lola and I scoured our fave department stores for suitable party clothes. As the birthday girl AND the birthday girl's best friend, we obviously had to look especially divine. In the end I bought the sweetest slip dress in shimmery lilac. Since it was a beach party, I was going to wear my dress with flip-flops, but v. v. cosmic flip-flops, decorated with big sparkly stars.

Unfortunately, my soul-mate and I got a *leetle* bit TOO wrapped up in our party plans, so much that we totally forgot the joint assignment we were supposed to be writing on the Hell dimensions!

We'd already blagged two extensions and Mr Allbright was clearly running out of patience. By a cruel coincidence, the Friday I'd unthinkingly picked for my birthday was also the absolute final deadline for our Hell dimensions assignment, a fact I totally failed to remember until my alarm went off on Friday morning.

As you've probably realised, angelic education is radically different to the human kind. For one thing, angel high school kids aren't known as 'pupils' they're called 'trainees', and I don't think a day goes by without our teacher banging on about how "you must remember you are being groomed to be the angel agents of the future!"

This is a fact we're not really likely to forget, especially as every heavenly high school kid over the age of twelve is expected to do hands-on work experience for a cosmic outfit we just call the Agency, a super-massive organisation dedicated to protecting Earth from the Powers of Darkness.

Obviously in an ideal Universe, they wouldn't send inexperienced angel kids on dangerous time-travel missions. But as the Agency doesn't have anything like enough trained agents to meet human demand, they end up using us to fill the gaps.

Given we're under so much pressure, wouldn't you think our teachers would be a *teensy* bit more understanding?

Yeah, right. You could have been on Planet Earth for *weeks*, wearing the same skanky combats, with nothing but angel trail mix between you and near-starvation, but the instant you get back, you'd better get that essay finished or you're in DEEP poo, let me tell you!

Anyway, when Friday morning arrived I woke up and blinked sleepily at the pretty patterns the heavenly sunlight was making on the ceiling, with a vague feeling there was something I should be doing,

Then I'm like, oh, duh! It's my birthday.

"Happy birthday, angel girl," I told myself happily. Then I let out a shriek.

I ran to Lola's room and hammered on her door.

My friend finally came to the door, with such a bad case of bed-hair you couldn't actually see her face.

"You *did* remember, didn't you?" I pleaded. "You *hate* handing in work late, I know you do. I bet you sat up all night."

"I fell asleep in the bath," she said shamefaced.

"*Lollie!* I was relying on you!" I tried to think. "OK, Mr Allbright's class isn't 'til eleven. If we sprint to the school library now we should just have time to dash off an outline. He'd have to see we're showing willing, right?"

"I thought Mr Allbright said all the serious Hell materials are in the town library?"

"OK, so we'll have to sprint faster. Grab your clothes, babe, and let's go, go, go!"

When we told the librarian what we wanted, she immediately asked to see our IDs then looked outraged. "I can't help you," she said stiffly. "The books on your list are *extremely* dark Hell texts which have to be kept in the vaults."

"Can't we read them down there?" Lola pleaded.

"Only senior trainees have pass keys," sniffed the librarian.

"Couldn't you make an exception?" Lola wheedled. "We won't tell anyone."

"I'm going to pretend I didn't hear that." She flounced off pushing a trolley loaded with returned books.

"Psst!"

We both jumped as Lola's boyfriend appeared grinning like the Cheshire cat through a gap in the bookshelves.

Having got our attention, he mooched over to meet us, wearing his usual uniform of ripped jeans and a scuzzy Astral Garbage T-shirt.

Don't tell Lola, but I still find it really hard to think of Brice as an angel. This is a true story, yeah? So I have to tell you that when I found out about his budding romance with my soul-mate, I was *not* a happy seraph. OK, so I've fancied a bad boy or two in my time, but I never went for an evil assassin!

At first we couldn't figure out why Brice kept popping up on our Time missions like a bad smell. Lola says it was destiny. I think it was more like desperation.

Brice was v. v. screwed up when he dropped out of angel school. I'm guessing that by the time we met him, he was totally sickened at the work he was doing for the Dark Agencies, and was already truly deeply homesick for Heaven. I think harassing angels was the closest he could get.

It can't have been easy, but somehow Michael our headmaster staunchly went on believing in Brice whatever, and to the shock of our entire school, eventually persuaded the School Council to take him back on probation.

As a born cosmic outlaw, Brice found his probationary period incredibly humiliating. He stuck it out though, passed his retakes, and recently moved up to the upper school where he's doing really well, Lola says.

All the same, you never quite know where that boy is coming from and Lola was visibly astonished, not to say deeply suspicious, to see him in the library. "Weren't you due at the Agency like an hour ago?"

"Nah, still got five minutes," he said carelessly. "Had to check something out in the Hell-dimensions vault before I take off. Thought you might like to borrow this?" Brice fished around in his pocket, made sure the librarian wasn't looking and surreptitiously flashed a blue glimmery card.

"You *stole* a celestial pass key!" I gasped.

"Do you want to say that a bit louder, sweetheart! For your information, I am now legally entitled to a pass key to any library in the Heavenly City."

"Sorry," I said humbly, "I keep forgetting you're a senior now."

He slid the pass key into a little gizmo on the wall and we saw a blue flash. Interesting clanking sounds came up the shaft.

Brice grabbed Lola's wrist to check her watch. "OK, seriously gotta go," he said in a rush. "The hell materials are in the lower basement. Save me some birthday cake, girls, yeah?"

We watched him disappear through the swing doors.

"We should really buy that boy a new T-shirt," I told Lola.

"*Carita*, let me tell you, Brice has a whole drawer full of Astral Garbage T-shirts. All exactly the same!"

"His hair looks soo much better though," I said approvingly.

Instead of the scary bleached mullet he had before, Brice now wore his naturally-dark hair in gelled spikes, with occasional blond flashes.

"Where's your bad boy going anyway?" I asked Lola.

"Not too sure," she said vaguely. "Some disturbed kid, I think he said."

"Bit sudden," I objected. "He was coming to my party last I heard."

"Yeah well, the Agency moves in mysterious ways and whatever."

A bell pinged and the lift doors slid open. I glanced round guiltily to make sure the librarian wasn't watching.

"It's OK, she's gone for her break," Lola hissed.

We hopped in the lift and went humming down for *miles*.

When the doors opened again, we both breathed, "Wow!"

From floor to ceiling, the library vaults were totally bathed in intense azure light. We tiptoed around in the eerie blue silence, trying to find the right section. The hard-core Hell materials turned out to be kept in special cases. You had to switch on a tiny light and read them through the glass.

Hell dimensions are more complicated than I'd realised; they have this whole evil ecosystem going on. I'm not sure how many hell species there are in total, but it's a *lot*!

Lola gave me a sly nudge. "Ooh, Mel, check out the cute hell doggie!"

I squeaked with revulsion. "Euw Lollie, it's *bald*!!"

We'd covered hellhounds in Dark Studies but it was the first time I'd seen a picture. Struggling not to laugh, Lola read out the old-fashioned angelic script under the engraving.

"'*These vile dogges do ofttymes attempte to walke on their hynde legges, which maketh them unpleasantly to resemble a drooling human!*' Oh, yuck – listen. It says, '*The hell dogges turdes smell vile and after sunset beginne to glowe a pallid green like to a subterranean fungus.*'"

I firmly snapped off Lola's little light. "We are never going to the Hell dimensions, Lollie, so we will *never* have to smell a hell dogge's pallid green poo. Now focus!"

We eventually succeeded in cobbling an outline together for Mr Allbright. As we panted in through the shimmery gates of the Angel Academy, I was ecstatic. My birthday could go ahead as planned!

"Babe, do you mind handing this into Mr Allbright?" Lola said unexpectedly. "I'll see you tonight at Rainbow Cove, OK?"

She raced off, dark curls flying.

"OK," I said to empty space.

Lola and I generally help each other get glammed up, but I just assumed she was organising a super-special birthday surprise.

When I got back from school I did all the things you do. I showered, washed and dried my hair, and put it up, leaving just a few cute little traily bits dangling down. I did my make-up, splashed on my fave perfume, and slipped into my shimmery lilac dress.

I was bubbling with excitement all the way to Rainbow Cove. I made my way down the winding cliff path, worn smooth and shiny from centuries of angels' feet, and OK, I did notice it was strangely quiet – also strangely dark.

I just thought they were hiding. I genuinely thought that when I reached the final bend, all my mates would leap out of the shadows, screaming, "Surprise!"

But when I came round the bend, there were no shadows. The beach was flooded with moonlight – and it was totally deserted.

No fairy lights, no music, no delicious buffet. Nothing.

Absolutely nobody had turned up.

Chapter Three

I sat down on the damp sand in my new dress and sobbed. I was so shocked and upset I was totally destroyed. Didn't my friends know how much this meant to me? Didn't they care?

Then all at once, as I wept and blubbered into my hands, I felt this... beautiful vibe.

When I looked up, snivelling and bewildered, it wasn't my friends I saw standing in front of me, but a group of shimmering light beings. I'd seen these pure luminous beings once before shortly after I arrived in Heaven. You could say they were my first glimpse of what it means to be a real angel, made of nothing but love and light.

Now my cosmic angels had come back!

I scrambled to my feet, respectfully tugging

down my dress as they silently gathered round me, and I heard their strangely impersonal voices in my head. "*So today's your birthday?*"

"Oh, about that," I gulped. "You see—"

The night was suddenly full of whizzy little rainbows: *zoom, zoom, zoom*. Too late I realised they were zooming towards me! As each miniature rainbow hit my energy field, it exploded into all its separate colours: scarlet and bright pumpkin orange, sunflower yellow and vivid emerald green, sky blue, midnight blue and violet. Then all these colours started to swirl into awesome cosmic-type patterns.

My energy field started flashing the exact same swirly patterns in the exact same rhythms. I'd like to tell you how long it went on, but I truly have no idea. Finally it was over.

"*Happy birthday, angel girl!*" the voices sang.

And they'd gone.

An instant later, twinkly pink fairy lights sprang on around the beach. A heavenly hip-hop beat started up.

"SURPRISE!"

My friends surrounded me, laughing and pelting me with sparkly confetti.

Lola flung her arms round me. "Happy birthday, *carita*! Did you enjoy your upgrade?"

"Is *that* what that was!"

There's me thinking I'm such a rebel, giving myself a DIY birthday, when it really *was* my birthday – my first true birthday as an angel! Angelic birthdays aren't about getting one year older (we're immortals, duh!). They're about getting more, you know... *angelly*!

"Open my pressie," Lola begged. She handed me a large box tied with about a zillion glittery ribbons, hovering anxiously while I carefully untied every one.

Inside was a lamp. It was literally constructed out of tiny jewel-coloured fairy lights, cunningly strung together in the shape of a v. cute, v. girly handbag.

I just stood there whispering, "Omigosh, Omigosh."

Lola's face crumpled. "Didn't I get the right one? Oh, Mel, I was *so* sure I'd got the right one."

"No, it is," I whispered. "It's exactly the same."

"I can change it. It's just you're always talking about that cool handbag lamp your mates got you for your thirteenth—"

I could still hear Lola anxiously burbling on, just as I could still see the fairy lights and Mo busily setting out my birthday buffet, but a part of me was back in our local Pizza Hut with my human mates…

We'd eaten as much as we could physically stuff in, and were chatting happily over pizza remains and slightly melted ice cream.

Suddenly Sky jumped up and rapped her glass. "Unaccustomed as I am to public speaking—"she started in a posh voice.

Jax blew bubbles rudely in her Coke, and Sky went into fits of giggles. "Stop it, you big pig! Tell her, Mel! She's ruining your big moment!"

"Your big moment, you mean," Jax snorted. "Look, just make your stupid speech, then we can go and see the movie!"

Sky self-consciously shook back her hair. "OK, um, I just want to say, don't think the Shocking Pinks are cheapskates, but we decided it would be better to club together so we could buy you something fabulous."

"I was going to nick it," Jax said shamelessly. "But Sky said nicking a birthday present would be bad karma."

Karmen put a gift-wrapped box on the table. "Tada!"

My friends watched expectantly as I unwrapped the exact twin to the lamp Lola had just given me in Heaven.

And just like now I was so amazed I didn't know what to say...

"You *hate* it, don't you?" Lola was saying tragically.

I finally found words. "Lola, It's PERFECT! I can't *believe* you got it for me."

"Step aside Sanchez, my turn to amaze the birthday girl!" Reuben practically shoved a tiny package into my hand. "As you can see, wrapping presents isn't my thing," he added cheerfully.

In fact, Reubs' present was already unwrapping itself; I just caught the glimmery crystal charm bracelet before it fell on the sand.

"It's totally luminous, Reubs," I breathed. "Where did you find it?"

He looked a bit embarrassed. "Millie made it. I had to give her all your personal info, then Millie picked charms which fitted. See there's a shell because you have this thing about the sea. This charm's an ancient angelic symbol for protection, and this star – but I guess you don't want to hear about every little bead, right?"

"Thanks, Reubs, I love it."

There was a slightly awkward pause.

"Well, better get back to my DJ duties," he grinned.

When he was out of earshot, I said, "I don't think I've met Millie?"

"Oh, she and Reubs have known each other for ever," Lola said.

It has *to be her,* I thought. During a late-night talk on our Limbo mission, Reuben let slip that he had a major crush, then flatly refused to give any more information. But a childhood sweetheart who made her own jewellery sounded exactly right for Reubs.

Until a few weeks ago, I'd always thought of Reubs as like my angel big bro. But since our soul-retrieval assignment we'd become just a tiny bit edgy with each other – in fact Reuben seemed to go out of his way to avoid being alone with me. I was worried I'd upset him. I kept asking Lola if he'd said anything to her. She insisted he hadn't, but I noticed she didn't deny he was upset. *Probably Millie's giving him a hard time,* I thought.

My party had been going for over an hour when I heard someone calling my name. I left the lights and the music without a thought, and ran down to the water's edge, where Michael was waiting.

"I can't believe you actually made it to my party!" I bubbled. "I heard you were away."

I was so happy to see him, I didn't even notice my headmaster wasn't smiling.

"I only just got back," he said in a quiet voice. "Melanie, I realise this is unfortunate timing, but I need you to come with me."

When I'm shocked, I do this silly high-pitched giggle. "You actually want me to leave my own birthday party—?"

Then I saw Michael's expression and my voice trailed off.

He looked unbelievably sad. "I'm afraid so. You see we've got to send you back home."

Chapter Four

Reflections flickered over my headmaster's face as he drove us downtown to the Agency building.

We've got to send you back home. The words went round in my head like a sound loop. I was far too scared to ask what was going on. Was I going to be kicked out of school? I'd come dangerously close to being expelled in my first term. Had I crossed a line with my cheeky DIY birthday?

Without taking his eyes off the road, Michael said, "You didn't do anything wrong, Melanie."

Still freaked from being snatched from my party, I wasn't sure I believed him. "Honestly?" I asked tearfully.

"You simply weren't ready for this until now."

I was just getting more confused. "I hate to be dense, but what's changed?"

He managed the glimmerings of a smile. "Have you forgotten what day it is already?"

"Oh *right*! You mean because of the upgrade!"

If I'd been thinking clearly, I might have asked why someone would need an angelic upgrade just to return home. But I wasn't thinking full stop. An amazing possibility had just occurred to me.

"Will I be able to see my family!"

"Of course," he said warmly. "You must see them while you're there."

"And my friends?"

Michael nodded.

"Omigosh, this is SO cool!" I almost kissed him! It wasn't a punishment; the *opposite* of a punishment in fact!! I'd passed some big angelic test and for my reward I was going to see the human beings I loved most in all the Universe.

As we drove into the underground car park, I sneaked a wary look at Michael. He still looked sad. Why would he be sad about such fabulous news?

"This IS just a visit, right?" I asked anxiously.

He manoeuvred into a space and switched off the engine. The pause was just long enough to make my heart turn over.

Our headmaster is such a total sweetie that I tend to forget he's also an archangel – a being so advanced you can't even begin to imagine what goes on in his head. As Michael met my eyes with his intense gaze, I felt like he was seeing deep into my soul.

"It's not just a visit, nor is it an assignment as yet – what we have here is an extremely delicate situation which could turn into your most challenging mission so far."

Since 'delicate' is polite Agency code for 'impossible', and 'most challenging' is code for 'really, really gruelling' my mind immediately flipped into overdrive. My first thought was that someone in my family might have had an accident or been taken ill. But then wouldn't Michael just say so?

I followed him anxiously through two sets of swing doors and into a lift. The doors closed and we went humming up into the clouds.

I watched the glowing numerals flash up, without really seeing them. I heard myself say, "It's one of my friends, isn't it?"

Michael gave a troubled sigh. "At this moment in time, all your friends are giving us cause for concern. I don't think you realise what a wonderful effect you had on those girls."

I almost fell over. *I'd* had a wonderful effect! It was *completely* the other way round!! It was Jax who'd taught me to stand up for myself. And Sky – well, you couldn't *not* be affected by Sky!

"I don't think so, Michael! I had NO luck stopping Jax shoplifting."

He flashed me his soul-piercing look. "Melanie, until you befriended Eve Jackson, no one ever showed the first sign of caring what happened to her."

My eyes filled with tears. "I didn't know."

"I thought perhaps you didn't," he said gently. "That's why I'm telling you now."

I was feeling rising panic. "Michael, I know I've had the upgrade and everything, but are you sure I'm up to this? Shouldn't you send a *real*, grown-up agent? Not to mention someone who's not so, you know, *involved*?"

He shook his head. "The Agency believes you know your friends better than any adult agent ever could. We have every confidence you would quickly detect any, erm, unsavoury influences."

The way he stressed 'unsavoury', I thought I'd sussed what he was telling me. "Don't say Karms is in love *again*! That girl has the worst taste in boys!"

Michael took a breath, "Melanie, before we go into Departures, I have to warn you that Park Hall is not exactly as it was when you left."

"I've only been gone eighteen months in Earth time," I teased. I was going to say, "Hopefully my mates won't *all* be wearing silver jump suits!" But at that moment I caught sight of myself and gave a shriek of horror.

"You've got to take me back to school first! I'm serious Michael! I can't go like this!"

No *way* could I go back to the gritty inner city wearing a shimmery lilac slip dress and flip-flops decorated with sparkly stars!

This time Michael actually chuckled. "You won't have to," he smiled. "I think you'll find my assistant has anticipated your needs!"

We hurried along gleaming corridors to Departures, where Michael's assistant, Sam, was waiting.

"I'd heard you make a habit of going on missions in your party clothes," he teased, "so I asked one of our stylists to pick out a few mix-and-match outfits." Sam handed me a large flamingo-pink carrier bag from one of my fave heavenly department stores. "And of course you get this delightful Agency flight bag with all the usual freebies!" he added with a grin.

I dashed off to the cloakroom to change. I was *so* impressed with my outfits. The Agency stylist had perfectly captured the inner-city vibe. For the outward journey I picked out a denim jacket, a cute flippy skirt and the *most* angelicious pink suede boots. Talk about going home in style!

I had a quick rummage through my flight bag. The contents seemed pretty standard – trail mix, Agency journal, comb, glow-in-the-dark pen, mobile – until I found the emergency flares.

Why the sassafras would I need *flares*?

I tinkered for a bit with the functions on my tiny Agency mobile, then had a naughty impulse and rang Lola.

She picked up straight away, like she'd been expecting my call. It sounded like my party was really totting up. I explained that I'd had to bail on my own celebrations because I was being sent back to my old human home.

"We had to zoom off to medieval France in the middle of mine, if you remember!" she yelled over the music.

"I wish you could come too," I said wistfully. I'd always had this big fantasy of taking Lola round all my fave human haunts.

"*Carita!* I'm so sorry. I didn't hear you properly before. Omigosh, you're going home? That's HUGE! But I know you're gonna do great!"

Feeling slightly tearful, I picked my way back through the crowds of celestial agents waiting for flights out of Heaven.

Eventually I spotted Michael chatting to one of the time technicians. This seemed like a good opportunity to sneak a word with his cute assistant.

"Nice boots!" Sam grinned when he saw me.

"I don't suppose the Agency mentioned how long I'll be staying?" I asked anxiously.

He shrugged. "As long as it takes basically, but I should think two weeks max. You'll be arriving on Friday afternoon as everyone comes out of school. Should make it easy to track down all your mates."

Sam handed me my angel tags, the little disk that tells everyone we're on official heavenly business. "And don't forget you're only a phone call away!"

Michael waved me over. "Any last minute questions, or concerns?" he smiled.

Only about a billion.

For the first time I was going to be travelling in one of the Agency's super-slick, one-angel-only time capsules.

As I ducked inside, I gave myself a stiff pep talk. *Melanie, you have survived Ancient Rome!* I told myself severely. You can *surely* cope with going back to Park Hall.

Two weeks max. Three hundred and thirty-six hours of Earth time. I could handle that.

The glass door purred smoothly into closed position.

The maintenance guy held up both hands. Ten seconds to go.

I waved and was surprised to hear a tiny tinkling of crystals. I'd forgotten to remove my bracelet. I nervously fingered the charms. *The shell is because you love the sea. This one is an ancient angelic symbol for protection...*

THREE, TWO. My capsule lit up like solar flares.

WHOOSH! I was blasted out of Heaven.

Reuben has tried to explain angelic time-travel to me soo many times you would not believe. As far as I'm concerned it's just magic!

Picture yourself hurtling through a vast nothingness, inside a fragile glass shell. Outside, starry streams of cosmic energy spiral off to form dazzling whirlpools, which get sucked into bigger, brighter whirlpools, and on into infinity.

You're looking at something so huge, so mysterious, your mind can't begin to take it in.

I have to pinch myself sometimes – like, *I'm travelling in Time. I'm an angel and I'm actually travelling in Time!!*

Yet this time, as I hurtled through eternity, I didn't glance outside once. I had almost completely forgotten I was an angel. I only knew I was going home, and I was overwhelmed with memories of my friends. These memories weren't just like moving pictures in my head. I felt like I was literally living through my experiences again, complete with all the emotions and sensations I'd had at the time. That first day at high school when we all hated each other on sight. The first time everyone slept over at my place and Sky forced us to dye her hair with henna, only we left it on so long it turned a screaming fire-engine red! The time me and my mates just took off to explore the city, without letting our parents know where we were going, then got back to find Karmen's mum had called the police...!

I'd been too busy to let myself miss them, you see – too busy trying to turn myself into an angel. Now I was being shown exactly how much I'd lost.

The flow of memories stopped just as the dramatic whooshing sensation of time came to a standstill.

Lights and shadows flickered on the other side of the glass. Any sounds that reached me were so faint and muffled, I could have been listening to bees buzzing in clover.

For no real reason, I started smoothing down my hair. It felt unexpectedly scary, knowing my old neighbourhood was outside, waiting to come into focus. I wondered if angels often returned to their human haunts and, if so, did they feel this same creepy sense of premonition, as if their worlds were about to smash into each other like two icebergs...

I glanced at my watch. They'd be out of school any minute.

Touching my tags for luck, I jumped down into twenty-first century London and shrieked in horror.

"Oh, noo, my *boots*!"

I was ankle deep in slush! No one had thought to tell me it would be the middle of winter! As I shivered in the blowing sleet, I'd have traded my granny for a big warm parka.

Cars and trucks crawled past, churning up the dirty snow, headlights barely visible through the gloom. Spine-thumping beats came from everyone's car stereos. That alone was enough to tell me I was back.

Checking that my bag was securely fastened, I set off towards the traffic lights, eyes straight ahead, every inch saying 'Don't mess with this angel girl!' I'd been home two seconds and I'd gone right back to being an inner-city chick!

On one level my old neighbourhood was how I remembered: same stink of traffic fumes and fast food, same hard-faced youths talking a mile a minute into their mobiles. The tattoo parlour was there and that whole-food shop which was run by Buddhists. It was all exactly the same. The only thing that had changed – was me.

I knew it wasn't fair but I couldn't stop comparing Park Hall with Heaven. I couldn't believe how tacky my neighbourhood had become. These are your roots, girl, I scolded myself, This was your human *home*. But it felt alien and ugly. As I trudged along with freezing slush seeping into my heavenly boots,

I don't think I've ever felt so lonely and mixed up, or so totally out of place.

I felt a glowing sensation in my chest, as if I'd swallowed a tiny slightly-too-hot potato. My inner angel had come online. Like soul-mates, inner angels are not an exclusively angel thing. Helix has been a part of me for ever, only now I actually listen to her wise advice! As usual she was totally on it.

"Are you sure these are *your* thoughts, sweetie?" she inquired.

"AAARGH!" I shrieked. "I have SO got to stop DOING that!!"

I do it *every* single time!! Pick up some local vibe and confuse it with my own feelings. EVERYONE in Park Hall feels lonely, mixed-up and out of place, except maybe the Buddhists!

"Thanks, Helix," I said huskily. "I was losing it big time."

"It's what I'm here for, babe. I think we're quite close to your school now. You might want to give yourself a *leetle* light boost."

I was already surrounded by criminals and drug dealers. I really couldn't see why Helix was stressing about my school. But I'm learning to respect her hunches. I obediently boosted my light levels and went on my way, feeling fabulously calm.

It was just as well. The neighbourhood vibes were dropping steadily. Without noticing I'd crossed the invisible border into the old run-down area folksily known as Bell Meadow. The houses were the same houses, the shops were the same shops, yet the low-level vibes made them seem weirdly threatening.

Because of Bell Meadow's humongous crime levels, my school was enclosed behind high brick walls topped with razor wire. Someone had sprayed angry graffiti: WE'RE GONNA GET YOU SHAY.

Outside the school gates, a few older youths hung around, looking vaguely dodgy in their big coats and hoods – might be selling drugs, but more likely they just had nowhere else better to go.

It was like the nightmare version of my dream-like arrival at the Angel Academy, only instead of glowing angel kids streaming in through glimmery pearl gates, hordes of tough, stressed-looking human kids jostled their way out of an ugly fortress-type entrance. Kids were swearing, smoking, bragging, screaming insults.

I'd been away too long. I'd forgotten what human schools can be like. The dark side of Park Hall

Community High School had been stealthily fading from my memories until it started to seem like one of those sunny vibey schools in hip-hop videos.

The initial stampede slowed, but there was no sign of my friends. I was baffled. It was Friday afternoon! No one hung about on Fridays if they had a choice.

I bet Miss Rowntree gave them a detention. *I'd better go in and find them,* I thought.

But Helix seemed uneasy. "Sweetie, trust me, it would be much wiser to wait out here."

"I'm not freezing my booty off for another hour! It's just a school, Helix! What can happen?"

Walking through the gates made me feel slightly sick, like I was having to push my way through an unfriendly force field. I just put it down to local vibes and cinched up my light levels.

The school doors were locked so I shimmered into the foyer.

"Yes, I *know* it's a dump, OK," I snapped, before Helix could get a word in. "It's a depressed area, what do you expect?"

Dump was not the word. Every single pot plant was dying, if not technically dead. The fish tank only contained slimy pebbles and a vandalised display case had been sloppily mended with tape.

Tired posters advertised a forthcoming production of GREASE, or, as one defaced poster now read, GROSS.

In the hall the drama group was in the process of murdering "Summer Lovin'". I couldn't believe it; Mr Lupton had been trying to get a production together since I could remember.

I started off down the corridor.

"Aren't you going to check the hall?" Helix asked in surprise.

"No point. My mates aren't the drama group type!"

I did try to make them audition once. For the same production coincidentally – and no, actually, it wasn't *only* because cute Kelsey Hickman was in the starring role! I happened to think we'd make pretty good Pink Ladies. I could totally picture us in those cute college-girl jackets.

But my mates flatly refused. They said it would ruin our edgy reputation. "I mean, PINK Ladies," Jax snorted. "How mushy and girly is that?" Jax and Sky thought all school clubs were tragically uncool.

"Aha!" I teased her. "So if it was the Shocking Pink Ladies, I suppose you'd do it!"

My friends were staring at me as if they'd had a vision.

"What? What did I say?"

Then Sky started jumping up and down and squealing. "Mel, you're a star! The Shocking Pinks is the PERFECT name for our posse!"

As I hurried along empty echoey corridors, I was so excited I kept forgetting to breathe.

When I reached our old classroom, I jumped up to peer in the window, absolutely knowing I'd see three fed-up girls and a grim Miss Rowntree doing her marking. I was actually giggling with nerves.

The room was empty.

They must be in the science lab. After Miss Rowntree, Mr Krishnamurti was the most keen on giving detentions. I started the long trek towards the science block.

"I should be wearing our colour," I giggled to Helix.

After school we'd gone rushing off to Claire's Accessories to hunt out the exact shocking pink items for our group makeover. We pinned shocking pink badges to our bags and re-covered our school exercise books in shocking pink paper; we totally went for it! Being a Pink gradually crept into every area of our lives. If you were down for any reason, one of us would firmly remind you to "Think Pink" –

Shocking Pink code for staying positive and hanging on to your dreams.

When you lived in a world that was one-hundred-per-cent grey, being a Shocking Pink was like a statement: "We're young, we're vibey and we're here!"

Sadly, like all Mr Lupton's previous productions, the cheesy musical that inspired this exciting transformation never came off. This time Kelsey's mum got picked up for shoplifting two days before the opening night.

Scared they'd be taken into care, Kelsey and his younger brothers did a runner. They were found weeks later living in a car. It seemed so unfair that he never got the chance to show what he could do. Kelsey would have made a totally brilliant Danny Zucco.

All humans have problems and my mates were no exception, but we definitely had it cushy compared to kids like Kelsey.

Our science block was in a new annexe along with the gym and computer labs. For reasons that probably made sense to the architects, the annexe was on the other side of the dual carriageway to the main school, connected by an ugly concrete bridge.

You know those motorway café bridges that sway in high winds? *Exactly* the same, except it wasn't glassed in, so it was *très* draughty. And even though it was a bridge, and obviously above ground, it had that icky subway vibe. This was possibly because the light bulbs were constantly being vandalised, so on winter afternoons, like this one, it was like walking down a long, windy and very nearly dark tunnel. I'd always hated walking over that bridge, but not nearly so much as Helix did.

"I'm getting a really *disgusting* vibe," she announced unhappily when we were like, a third of the way across.

"So why are you telling *me*?" I'd got it into my head that Helix was criticising my school, so of course I felt like I had to be Park Hall High School's number one fan.

All along the bridge someone had daubed YOU'RE GOING TO GET YOURS SHAY. In my day graffiti always got nuked by the school cleaners virtually the same day it appeared.

I didn't want to admit it, but I was increasingly freaked. It wasn't just the subway vibes, it was the *smell*. Our science block was never exactly fragrant, but today the air was quite repulsively whiffy.

"What's that?" Helix asked abruptly. "I heard something."

"You're doing my head in, Helix!" I snapped. "It's the wind, OK?"

"Something like *footsteps*. And a weird whining."

"Just take a chill pill, will you! It's probably one of the cleaning ladies singing!"

"There it is again!"

I peered nervously into the dusky gloom at the end of the tunnel, and caught a tiny movement. At the same time I heard a stealthy pad-padding, so soft and furtive that all the tiny hairs stood to attention on the back of my neck.

All at once I almost gagged. "Urgh!" I clamped my hand over my nose. "That is *SO* rank!"

"We should get off this bridge," Helix said urgently. "This is not a good place for angels."

"We can't," I gulped. "We haven't checked the lab."

I felt my knees totally give way, like I'd been kicked from behind. Next minute I was grovelling on my hands and knees.

I just exploded. "Are you *mad*!! Did you just trip me up?"

"And I'd do it again if I had to. I want you to look down NOW!"

My inner angel seemed so frantic that I obeyed. Then I saw the horrible thing she'd been trying to warn me about and screamed.

Chapter Five

My face was inches from a pile of glistening supernatural turds.

I know this is way too much information, but in the semi-twilight of the bridge, the pallid green Hell poo did actually seem to glow.

For a moment I was hypnotised with horror.

What if I'd touched it?

This thought made me want to beam home to Heaven and shower with rose-scented angel shower gel for like, a year.

"This isn't *right,*" I whispered.

I suddenly unfroze, scrambling to my feet.

If there was green hell poo, then there had to be hellhounds too!

Omigosh, the kids! Humans rarely register cosmic

phenomena, but if a pack of hellhounds crashed their rehearsal, it could still seriously damage their wellbeing.

I hurtled back along the bridge.

"Sorry I decked you, babe," Helix said apologetically.

"No, you had to, honestly," I gargled, still trying not to breathe. "I should have listened."

As I'm sure you realised, hellhounds can't simply wander into the human dimension and poo wherever they feel like it. Ok, so their evil masters are allowed to travel freely throughout the Universe, but there's a total cosmic ban on evil pets, or any other kind of hell trash.

When I got back to the foyer, I could hear a buzz of voices. I assumed the cast were taking a break, then I heard sudden angry shouting.

"Omigosh, my mates *are* in there!" I gasped. "Sounds like Karmen's got a major part!"

But when I charged in, it was obvious no one was rehearsing. The kids were shrugging on their coats, looking incredibly cheesed-off.

"I'm just as disappointed as you are," Mr Lupton was saying. "But there's no way we're ready to go on in a fortnight. Tonight was a shambles and you know it. We've lost far too many cast members."

I wilted with disappointment.

The girl who was giving Mr Lupton a hard time was remarkably similar to my mate, but she had a cute layered bob. Karmen would *never* cut her hair.

"I can't believe you're doing this!" this girl was yelling. She was right up in Mr Lupton's face, almost spitting with fury.

"It's not the *kids'* fault they've got problems! If you really cared about us, sir, you'd understand."

The girl really did look amazingly like Karmen. But shy little Karms was too timid to yell at anyone, let alone a teacher.

Mr Lupton hitched up his baggy cords. "I do care," he said unhappily. "But there's a limit to—"

"It's STUPID to stop now. We've all worked SO hard!"

"I'm sorry, my answer's still 'no'."

He tried to turn away but she just barged in front of him and continued harassing him. "What if I could get them all back?" she begged. "What if I rounded them up and we worked flat out all day Sunday?"

This musical had been Mr Lupton's pet project for years and you could tell he totally yearned to be convinced. "But we can't put this right in two weeks," he said unhappily.

"So ask Mrs Threlfall if she'll let you take us out of lessons until we finish the play! We can DO this, sir. They build gardens in a poxy weekend on TV! Give us one last chance. *Please?*"

It *was* her! That slight lisp on 'poxy'. Karm's voice was unmistakable now.

But where were the others? She wouldn't have joined the drama group by herself, so why weren't Sky and Jax here to back her up?

Mr Lupton gave another nervous hitch to his trousers. "All right, one last chance," he sighed. "I want everyone here by 9.30 on Sunday morning and we'll just see how it goes."

To my amazement, all the cast members cheered.

"We won't let you down, Mr Lupton, I swear," one girl told him.

"You're all right, man," one of the boys grinned.

"At least one teacher believes in us," said his mate.

Was this REALLY my school? Not to diss my old mates, but Park Hall pupils are not natural joiners. Dreamers yes. Antisocial losers definitely. Joiners? No way!

Having saved their production, you'd think Karmen would want to hang out with the rest of the cast, but she just grabbed her parka and flew out of the door.

Panicking that I'd lose her again, and forgetting all about hellhounds and earth angels, I zoomed in pursuit.

Outside my school it was one long traffic jam. A double decker was slowly inching past the school gates. Karms hopped on. I followed her up to the top deck and took the seat beside her.

My vibes were still tuned to angelic, not human, reality, so Karms couldn't see me, but she might be able to sense me.

"Well, this feels weird," I told her softly. "You look *so* different, Karms – *très* grown-up!"

It wasn't just the new hairstyle. It was Karmen herself. My Karms was constantly badgering us to tell her what to think or what to wear. It drove us *nuts*, yet you felt like you had to take care of her. But there was nothing helpless about the girl sitting next to me. She was like a human laser beam; all her energy was focused on a single point: how to make this production happen. In the old days, I'd have assumed she was pursuing some boy in the drama group – some skanky loser of a boy – but you couldn't see *this* Karmen going for losers.

My mate tensed up. She'd spotted someone in the street. She whipped her phone out of her pocket, tapped in a pre-set, and yelled, "Where the HELL were YOU? You know how many kids turned up tonight? *EIGHT!* It was humiliating, Jax!"

Determined to see my second Pink before the bus moved off, I half-dived across Karmen, peering out of the steamed-up glass.

Was that *truly* Jax down there? No WAY!

I'd never have recognised her if Karms hadn't used Jax's name. My friend's natural red-brown hair had been dyed neon-sign pink. She had so many metal piercings it looked like she had bristles.

Jax was gesturing angrily, clearly not in the mood to co-operate.

Karms huffed with annoyance. "No, because I bought us some more time, didn't I? He's agreed to let us rehearse all day Sunday."

The bus chugged away again, leaving Jax behind.

"I will NOT let it go." Karmen's voice was shaking now. "No I'm not listening to you, Jax. Show up on Sunday or you're in big trouble."

She rang off and stared unseeingly out of the window until we reached her stop. I followed her off the bus feeling like Alice when she fell down the rabbit hole. Nothing made sense.

I'd just seen Karmen fighting for the right to embarrass herself in public. Shy little Karmen who used to be too chicken to ring out for a pizza! Meanwhile Jax, who'd always been a wee bit rough around the edges, had turned into the teenage harpy from hell!

By this time it wouldn't have surprised me if Karmen's parents had become total nudists. I followed her nervously into the small terraced house, but to my relief, everything was exactly like I remembered. It even had that same homey, very faintly spicy smell.

Mrs Patel had The Be Good Tanyas playing on the stereo as she prepared the evening meal. Karm's parents were crazy about country music. They'd wanted to name their only daughter after one of those big-haired country singers, Dolly, Loretta-Sue, or whoever, but that didn't go down with the grandparents, so they compromised with 'Karmen Asha'.

Karmen used to reckon, out of all the Pinks, her mum liked me best; Karms said she thought I had a sweet smile.

I imagined what her mum would say if she knew who was sitting at their breakfast bar. "Karmen's been telling me you're an angel now, Melanie! Isn't that absolutely *fantastic*! You must try some of these sweets. No, darling, eat as many as you like. That way I won't be tempted!"

Over sounds of efficient chopping, Karmen and her mum chatted about what to buy one of the cousins for a wedding present.

If you didn't know Karmen, you could have been fooled into believing everything was normal. But I was deeply worried, not to say shocked. *My* Karms had to rush to the phone every five minutes to call her mates. Sometimes she'd ring each of us in turn just to ask which top we thought she should wear next day.

Listen – I sat at that breakfast bar for over an *hour* and Karmen didn't phone the other Pinks ONCE. But that wasn't the most shocking thing. When it finally hit me, I couldn't believe I hadn't noticed.

Karmen wasn't wearing our colour.

That's why she didn't phone. That's why the others refused to support her at the rehearsal.

"Omigosh," I whispered.

The Shocking Pinks had broken up!!

If it wasn't for Helix I'd probably be sitting in the Patels' kitchen today going, "Omigosh, Omigosh."

Unlike me, my inner angel has excellent control of her emotions. She said calmly, "This is upsetting, but we need to know what's going on with these girls."

I tried to pull myself together. "Should I check Karm's room?" I gulped. "Look for clues to her state of mind?"

"Exactly what I was thinking," Helix agreed.

I found clues all right, and they didn't reassure me about my friend's state of mind. GREASE posters plastered over the walls, a GREASE DVD cover beside the DVD player, a GREASE minidisc on top of her minidisc player... I could go on.

"This isn't being *focussed,*" I said in dismay. "This is being *obsessed*! This is Park Hall, Helix! IF they get this production together, *which* I doubt, they'll be lucky to sell two tickets."

I don't know why it took me so long to see the photograph – maybe because Karmen had put it in such a big fancy frame.

It had been taken on our mad day out, minutes after we got off the London Eye. A helpful tourist took it with Karm's digital camera. In the picture we've got exactly the same smiles.

For some reason Karmen had put a scented candle in front of the picture, and a silk rose. The rose was bright pink.

I felt something slam shut inside my mind. Like, *don't go there.* Lots of girls had candles and flowers in their rooms. It didn't mean anything morbid.

I heard the sound of a key turning in the front door. Karmen's dad was home. He dropped his bag and went into the kitchen.

"Friday night!" he sighed. "Two whole days of freedom!"

I peeped out of my friend's room in time to see him grab Karmen's mum and dance her round madly to the Tanyas.

I had a sudden longing for my own family. We had this big Friday ritual. I'd pick Jade up from her after-school club, we'd meet Mum out of work, then the three of us would go to the Cosmic Café. It didn't look much from outside, but the food was out of this world. If he wasn't on call-out, Des would join us later.

I'd been trying my best to act like an angel on a mission, but now the ache was so strong, it was an actual pain in my chest.

I want to see them.

In a heartbeat I was standing on the street opposite the Cosmic Café, icy sleet blowing in my eyes and mouth.

"*Woo!*" I said in awe. "Did I even say that out loud?"

Next minute I was charging across the busy road, literally morphing through cars and buses in my desperation to get to them.

To you they'd have looked like an ordinary London family in a cheap and cheerful café. To me, they looked like Christmas morning. I felt like I was going to explode with love. There they all were! Big bald Des pointing out something on the Specials board. Jade pulling on my step-dad's sleeve. And Mum had totally changed her hair!

"They're so *beautiful*," I whispered.

I was so focused on the little scene inside the café, I didn't register the otherworldly personnel carrier nosing up to the curb. I didn't suspect a thing until two sinister reflections loomed up in the misted glass. Next minute, hands gripped my arms, pinning them to my sides so I couldn't move, and I was being dragged, screaming, away from my family.

A hand clamped down firmly over my mouth. I felt myself helplessly lifted off my feet and bundled into a vehicle. The engine was still running. There was a swoosh and a clunk as the doors slid shut and we started to move off.

I scratched and bit my unknown kidnapper thrashing about in my frenzy to get free. I didn't even care if I poisoned myself with PODS toxins.

"OK, bad joke!" a voice admitted. "Listen, I'm going to take my hand away on a count of three, but DON'T bite! I promised my girlfriend I'd get back in one piece. One, two, th—"

My eyes had been screwed tight shut. Now they flew wide open.

"BRICE?" I said in disbelief.

Chapter Six

"Hey check those, real angel tooth marks!" Lola's boyfriend showed his hand to his mate, seeming almost proud.

The other angel boy laughed. "Sure that's an *angel* chick? Seems more like a hell vixen to me!"

Brice waggled his eyebrows. "Mel can be quite feisty when she wants to be!"

They went on joking over my head in that maddening way boys do all across the Universe. Now I was over the first shock, I was livid. I gave Brice a hard thump. "You gave me a heart attack you pig!! I thought you were PODS!"

He fended me off laughing. "I couldn't resist, you looked so sweet and goofy, darling. You were totally away with the fairies."

I just glared. I didn't tell him about my family. I couldn't.

Brice's mate had the grace to look embarrassed. "Sorry, that was a stupid thing to do, " He stuck out his hand. "I'm Hendrix."

Woo, I thought, he's *really* fit.

I shyly shook his hand. "Nice to meet you."

I flashed an evil look at Brice. "What are you doing here, dirt bag? Apart from scaring me out of my skin?"

He looked slightly shifty. "Oh, you know, making the inner city a better place. Beating Hendrix at pool."

"In your dreams!" Hendrix told him.

"Omigosh, Hendrix, you're an EA!" I realised suddenly. "I've got to report a cosmic anomaly at Park Hall High School. Some hell beastie got into my school – and *pooed*, can you believe?"

I thought I saw a weird look pass between them.

Hendrix said quickly, "We'll get someone on it, don't worry."

The angel carrier had been accelerating steadily while we were talking. Suddenly there was a violent lurch and I was virtually thrown into Hendrix's arms as the van began hurtling through traffic at breakneck speed.

"I should buckle up sweetheart," Brice advised. "Unless you *enjoy* cuddling Hendrix. Jools is a bit of a speed freak."

I hastily unpeeled myself, pulling a hideous face at Brice. "Does he *always* drive like this?"

"She," Brice corrected.

"And yes, Jools only drives in top gear," grinned Hendrix.

Jools was now driving the wrong way up a one-way street. It was a heavenly vehicle, totally harmless to human road users, but I had to cover my eyes. We finally screeched to a stop.

I clambered out of the angel carrier on jelly legs, then rubbed my eyes. I'd walked down Matilda Street just about every day on my way to and from school, and never seen this elegant shimmery house. That's because it was an Agency house which had been invisibly slotted into a shabby human terrace.

"I had no idea we had houses on Earth!" I breathed.

"There's a few," said a warm voice. A girl swung down from the driver's seat. She wore a long rainbow-striped scarf draped over her combat jacket. "How many are there now, Hen?"

Hendrix shrugged. "It must be in the thousands. Oh, this is Jools, who was completely against us kidnapping you by the way!"

"I was," she sighed. "But Brice—"

"—is a terrible influence, I know," I joked.

With her big boots, old combats and an even older cap jammed over beaded braids, Jools was probably not your nan's idea of an angel. But she did look exactly like girls I knew in Park Hall. EAs usually like to adopt the styles and cultures of their local human community.

Jools held up her angel tags to a device on the wall. There was a brief blue shimmer. The door slid open and Brice, who seemed to think he was an honorary earth angel, grandly ushered me inside.

I was blown away. I couldn't believe I was still in the middle of a twenty-first century human city. The vibes in the Agency house were so pure I could have been back in Heaven.

An angel girl in combat gear came hurrying down the stairs. "Oh hi," she smiled, and disappeared into one of the downstairs rooms.

I heard a steady hum of voices coming through the door.

"That's the EA communications centre for this area," Jools explained. "Like the Angel Watch centre, but much smaller, obviously."

I peered curiously round the door and saw twenty plus agents at their work stations, jabbering quietly into headsets. "Where did the incident take place?" one agent was asking her caller. "Any signs of You Know Who? OK, we'll get you some backup. Do the best you can until then."

"We'll show you round later," Jools promised. "You could probably do with a rest."

"I'll carry that," Hendrix said, taking my bag.

"You think you're so smooth," Brice told him.

As they shepherded me up flights of stairs, I was trying to take in the sheer scale of the Agency safe house.

In one open-plan area, trainees calmly worked at computers which had up to ten different streams of cosmic data racing hectically across their screens at any one time. Next door a lone trainee was minding banks of monitors, all of which showed local trouble spots. One had a split screen which showed the same house from different angles.

"That house used to be a vet's," I said in surprise.

"Those were the good days then," the trainee

said grimly. "The life forms that live there now aren't exactly man's best friend."

I felt a shiver go through me. "PODS live there now?" I'd taken my little sister past that house on the way to her tap lessons.

"Officially it's inhabited by humans," Hendrix explained.

"Just not any you'd like to meet," Jools commented.

I'd met humans like that on previous missions: people so closely involved with the Dark agencies, they were half-PODS themselves.

"Much activity today?" Hendrix asked the trainee.

He shook his head. "Just the usual."

We toiled up a final flight of stairs. A boy angel was pacing the landing with his mobile.

"No, since he started with the kick boxing, he's much more confident, like a different boy..."

I followed the others into a big studenty sitting room. Two angel girls looked up and smiled, then went back to chatting. A boy was stretched out on one of the sofas, apparently asleep.

I've seen EAs in just about every time you can think of, but seeing them in my old neighbourhood made me so happy I wanted to cry. I'd been rubbing shoulders with angels all those years and didn't even know! *I LOVE my job*, I thought tearfully. *I have the best life* ever.

"Can anyone else smell that stink?"

I came back to Earth to see Jools screwing up her nose in disgust, making me notice a tiny star-shaped stud for the first time.

"Mel found hell turds at the school," Hendrix said super-casually.

Her expression changed. "Not again," she said half to herself. She turned, flashing her warm smile. "Mel, I hate to be a pain, but I think you picked up something whiffy on those beautiful boots."

"Oh, I *thought* I could—!" I nervously inspected one boot sole, hopping to keep my balance. "Oh, no, I *did*!" I wailed. "This is SO embarrassing!"

"Give them here," laughed Hendrix.

Holding my boots by their tops, he gallantly whisked them away.

Jools started madly spraying everything in sight with some kind of heavenly Febreze. "You must think I'm so rude," she said apologetically. "I just have this incredibly sensitive sense of smell."

I couldn't believe I'd trekked hell dog poop into an angel house!

"I tamed a hell puppy once," Brice said with a straight face.

My poopy boots were instantly old news. Every angel in earshot stared at him in horror. Even the boy who'd been snoozing sat up open-mouthed.

Jools giggled nervously. "Brice, I never know when you're joking!"

"It's true," he insisted. "He was a smart little guy. Answered to his name and everything."

"Yeah, yeah," laughed Jools. "What did you call him? Fluffy?"

"I called him Bob," Brice said with dignity.

"Why would anyone call a hellhound Bob?" spluttered the boy.

"You think I should have named him Fang?" Brice snapped. "He was a little motherless puppy, man!"

Jools suddenly looked horrified. "My manners! Did we even introduce you?"

I shyly shook my head.

"We've given you such a terrible welcome," she wailed. "First the guys kidnap you off the street, then we tell you have stinky boots, and *then* we don't even— OK, let's do it now. This is Delphine, this is Tallulah, and Sleeping Beauty here answers to Dino."

I stood there in my socks, nodding and smiling, but absolutely nothing was going in.

"When did you last eat, angel girl?" Brice interrupted.

Hendrix had reappeared with my decontaminated boots. "I could murder a pizza personally – how about you guys?"

"You get *pizza*!" I said amazed. "You don't just live on trail mix?"

"Don't talk to me about that stuff!" said Jools with feeling. "Girl, it gives me the *worst* wind!"

I creased up laughing. "Doesn't it!"

Minutes later Jools and I were in the shared kitchen, hungrily tearing up pizza. The boys were eating theirs in the TV room.

"I'm so grateful I ran into you guys," I told her happily.

"It's great cosmic timing," she smiled. "My room mate is actually away on a course, so you can have her bed – if you don't mind sharing," she added quickly.

"Are you *kidding*? I was worrying I'd have to sleep in a doorway!"

Jools was carefully picking off her sweet corn. "Is it OK to ask what you're doing here?"

"You can ask," I mumbled through too-hot pizza. "All I know is my mates are in some kind of trouble."

"Have you managed to hook up with them yet?"

"Not hooked up, exactly," I sighed. "I've seen two of them."

Jools was a great listener. She gave me her total attention as I described the disturbing changes in my friends.

"You're sure they've broken up finally and for ever?"

"It certainly feels pretty final," I sighed.

Jools looked sympathetic. "It happens."

"I know, I know, people move on."

"Is that how it feels? Like they just moved on?"

I shook my head. "Actually it doesn't."

While we were talking, Brice wandered in with Hendrix and a couple of boy EAs.

"So where are we going, girls?" Hendrix demanded. "It's Friday night! We can't just stay in eating pizza!"

"There's that new club down the road," Jools suggested. "They're getting that DJ – what's his name again?"

"Ruff Justice?" Brice said unexpectedly.

"How come you *always* know this stuff?" I marvelled. "You got here just before me!"

"You'll come with us, won't you Mel?" Jools asked hopefully.

I shook my head. "It's been a really long day."

Brice patted my head. "Mel's going to curl up in her jammies, aren't you, and reread the intro to the Angel Handbook?"

I swatted him. "I got to chapter two, for your information!"

"You did well!" Jools laughed. "That book is *soo* heavy going."

This is exactly why Lola and I are going to write our Cosmic Survival Guide, but this is still a big secret between me and my soul-mate, so I kept my lips v. firmly sealed.

Jools slung an arm round my shoulder. "Come on Mel, don't you want to see how earth angels party?"

"Yeah!" I decided.

In the end a whole gang of us went down in the angel carrier, including Tallulah and Dino, the Sleeping Beauty boy.

You could feel the bass line pumping from the other side of the street. I felt a naughty buzz as we waltzed past security. I thought we all looked quite groovy. Brice had put on a fresh T-shirt under his leather jacket (I know!). I'd borrowed a sweet skirt from Jools and a cute top which said SHINE ON.

The club was already packed out.

Hendrix gave me his flirty smile. "Want to show the humans some real dancing?"

Next to flirting with good-looking earth angels, dancing is one of my all-time favourite activities! But when angels and humans dance in the same space, ohh – it's PURE magic.

As the night went on I was amazed to see some of the human dancers picking up on our dance style. At times the DJ actually seemed to sense our vibes. "I'm feeling some *sweet* energy in the house tonight," he kept saying. "You Park Hall people must have *serious* auras. Yeah man, there's enough lies and illusion in this world, but you guys are still keeping it real."

"We're trying, Justice, we're trying," yelled one of the earth angels, and the entire angel contingent cheered!

At that moment I wouldn't have swapped with the old Mel Beeby for anything. Even Brice appeared to be having a good time.

But this was Park Hall, so obviously it couldn't last.

Around two in the morning, Jools and Hendrix got a call – a gang fight with suspiciously high levels of PODS interest.

Chapter Seven

I was up for anything by this time. Just as well, because we were in for one of Jools' white knuckle drives. We bombed over speed bumps, taking interesting short cuts which *definitely* weren't in the A to Z.

At last we drove into a dead end behind some council flats.

There's a thing our Dark Studies teacher calls 'miasma': a sticky dark aura which collects wherever Dark agents gather together.

"Yup," said Brice grimly. "Your bad boys definitely have an audience."

"How big?" Hendrix asked.

"Hard to tell – they're kind of overexcited so they keep changing shape." Brice was using what me and Lola call his 'Dark radar', a disturbing ability to detect Dark agents even when, like now, they weren't in human disguise.

As we pulled up, there was another shock. For some reason the call centre hadn't thought to mention this was a girl fight.

I couldn't tell how many girls were milling about. There was one streetlight and that was on the blink. You just caught dramatic glimpses – a gold hoop glinting in an earlobe, a sneery mouth, a flash of designer trainers. Smashed cider bottles littered the ground; some gang members had been doing some serious underage drinking.

I just didn't get why those creeps were watching. This kind of teen ruck was a depressingly routine event in my neighbourhood, yet the local Dark entities had not only got wind of it before it started, they'd turned out in the snow to get a ringside seat.

"They're not moving in on the girls?" Jools asked Brice.

He shook his head. "Just perving on the hate vibes."

"Let's keep it that way, guys," she said. "Boost your light levels everyone – and good luck!"

Everyone piled out of the angel carrier. We'd arrived just as things were finally hotting up.

With a shriek of rage, a girl hurled herself at another girl from the rival gang, bringing her crashing to the ground.

The girls rolled around in the slush, grunting with effort as they grabbed at each other's earrings and tried to rip out clumps of hair, while invisible beings from rival cosmic agencies watched.

According to our Dark Studies teachers, the safest technique for clearing Dark entities from the area is to raise the vibes. Sounds hippy dippy, doesn't it? Like we hold hands in a circle and chant?

What we actually do is beam incredibly high-octane angel vibes from the palms of our hands.

Raising vibes in the middle of a gang fight is probably a lot like trying to meditate in a tsunami. You get a peaceful little vibe going and DOOF! A wave of pure cold evil knocks you over and you have to struggle all the way back to shore.

Brice couldn't be fussed with all that, he just went over and started knocking the sassafras out of the creeps, and after a while Hendrix went to help out.

The first girl had managed to kick her opponent away. Breathing fast, she scrambled to her feet and immediately put up her fists. "Anyone who disses my girls is going to have to kiss these!" she screamed.

The girl started a jittery war dance, aiming fake punches with a bit of kickboxing thrown in. In the strobing lamplight, she didn't seem human; she was just this girl fighting-robot with neon pink hair. Scuffing up ice, she leapt into the air like a girl ninja. FLASH. Her gang's name jumped off the back of her jacket. SHOCKING PINKS.

I almost cried out. It was Jax!

There was a CRUMP as someone from the rival gang took her on, and was sent sprawling. Screaming like witches, other girls flung themselves into the mayhem. I saw girls viciously gouging other girls' eyes, long nails raking down cheeks, and Jax was totally pounding some other girl into the ground.

That's the problem with cosmic energies – you can't predict which way they'll go. If you've got dense Dark energy and you add pure Light energy to the mix, things generally calm down – on the other hand they can go totally thermonuclear...

Then again, sometimes the PODS just don't want the hassle."Don't look so upset, they're going," Brice said in my ear.

Minutes later, both gangs backed down. They called out half-hearted taunts, but that was just to save face.

Jax took off running.

"I want to make sure she's OK!" I told the others.

"You *know* her?" Earth angels don't shock easily, but Jools did look surprised.

"She's my friend," I told them shakily. "She's really not like this, I swear."

"We'll take you," said Hendrix immediately.

We didn't have to drive far. Jax was just going home.

She stumbled past garages and wheelie bins until she reached the block of low-rise flats where she lived with her mum, dad and four brothers. It was one of the old-style blocks – no lifts, just flights of concrete steps on the outside, with a row of scruffy doors going off each landing.

Leaving Hendrix to mind the vehicle, we followed Jax up to the fourth floor. Snow flurries blew in over the balcony as Jax fumbled for her key.

Inside, the hall smelled of fag smoke and old booze.

I'd been to the Jackson's once before, about six months before I died. Jax made me wait in the hall while she got her coat. I didn't know about vibes in those days, but even then I couldn't imagine anyone laughing in this flat, or bringing someone a bunch of flowers.

Behind the closed sitting-room door, Jax's mum and dad were going on at each other.

Jax stumbled to her room, fell on to her bed and crashed out, fully clothed. She didn't look like a girl fighting-robot now. She looked like a sad little kid.

I couldn't believe the state of my friend's room: rubbish and dirty clothes everywhere. Worst of all were the vibes. Even her cactus had croaked.

We all knew it would take more than one visit to put Jax's problems right, but we got to work boosting the light levels straightaway. After about ten minutes, you could feel a definite difference.

Jools whispered, "I think that's the best we can do for now."

Jax half-turned on to her front and started snoring. The neon pink of the gang's name exactly matched the streaks in her hair.

She'd been so proud to be a Shocking Pink. Now she'd ripped off our name and turned it into an ugly battle cry and I didn't know why.

Tell the truth, Mel.

The truth is, I was *scared* to know why.

We left Jax's flat and hurried back downstairs to Hendrix, who was still in the van.

I heard myself say, "I'll catch up with you guys later. I've got one more friend to check on."

"Want some company?" Brice offered.

I tried to smile. "No, thanks, I need to clear my head."

"Take this," he said gruffly, shrugging off his jacket. "Park Hall is a lot colder than Heaven."

I set off to the Nolans' place, keeping my head down against the wind and snow. Brice's jacket was way too big and, despite Lola's best efforts, it held a whiff of what we jokingly call his 'Dark angel' smell.

Actually I didn't mind it *that* much – maybe that's because I felt a bit like a Dark angel myself.

Jools had asked if maybe my friends had just moved on. But when you move on, isn't that because your friendship doesn't fit you any more? Well, that wasn't Jax and Karmen. They hadn't just *changed*. It felt like they were being driven by some scary force and I had a bad feeling it was this same force which had torn their friendship apart.

I began to run, half-limping, half-sliding, down the icy street in my borrowed shoes, but I had the terrible sense that I was already too late. Because, if Karms and Jax had both gone off the rails, what in the world was happening to Sky?

Chapter Eight

Unlike Jax, Sky Nolan never broke any actual laws (that she told us about anyway), but of all the Shocking Pinks she was definitely the most outrageous.

The first time we went out together, we were all saying what we wanted to be. When Sky announced that she intended to be a stand-up comic, no one even blinked. We *totally* believed she could do it! That's how charismatic Sky was.

Sky was a fabulously exciting person to have as your friend, but you wouldn't want to cross her. If you did, Sky would find a way to make you pay. Like that time she got back at Miss Rowntree by painting cooking oil on the blackboard. The next time our teacher picked up a piece of chalk and tried to write, absolutely nothing showed up!

Weeks later we were all at Karmen's, kidding around on her karaoke machine, when Sky went into hysterics and finally let us in on the joke.

"I can't believe you just went off and did that all by yourself!" Karmen said amazed.

"Believe it!" Sky said coolly, flicking back her hair. "Sky Nolan is an independent operator!"

She made it sound like she was this romantic free spirit. But it was because Sky basically didn't trust anyone. Even if she liked you, Sky had to keep you at a safe distance.

At various times, Sky convinced each of us that we were her best friend. It was delicious being Sky's best friend. She'd plan little treats for you, lend you her coolest clothes and tell you incredibly intimate things about her personal life. Then one day you'd wake up to find you'd been mysteriously put on hold and it was someone else's turn.

All the Pinks got burned in this way, yet always when it was our turn to be Sky's favourite again, we'd kid ourselves this time would be different.

I'm making it sound like she wasn't a very nice person – and maybe she wasn't – but she was *truly* loveable.

She also had really bad problems at home.

I don't know if I mentioned Sky's mum wasn't too stable? One morning Sky came to school and she couldn't stop smiling.

"My mum was in such a great mood last night," she bubbled. "She made us a totally *massive* stack of pancakes. Of course, Olly insists he's big enough to toss his own pancake, doesn't he, and now it's permanently stuck to the kitchen ceiling!"

In those days Sky still hoped that one of her mum's good times would eventually stick for good, like Olly's pancake. Then, after years of being a deeply depressed single mum, Mrs Nolan got a boyfriend.

For a time everything seemed rosy. Sky's mum was happy. Sky's little brothers totally worshipped Dan and Sky adored him.

Late one night Sky called me on my mobile, to tell me her mum had locked her out. There'd been thunderstorms all day and Sky was terrified of storms; she sounded hysterical.

I fetched my step-dad, who threw on some clothes and drove off to pick her up. She looked half-drowned when he brought her back, rainwater dripping off her nose, hair in sodden rats' tails. Her mum hadn't even let her take her *shoes*.

Mum ran her a hot bath while I made up the sofa bed and dug out a clean T-shirt for Sky to sleep in. An hour later, I was still trying, not very successfully, to get back to sleep, when I heard her creep into my room.

I silently moved over to let her climb in. I could feel tiny tremors going through her, like she was getting flu. I tentatively touched her and Sky sobbed out, "I just wish I'd never been born."

I stroked her back while she cried and eventually she felt able to choke out what had happened. She and her mum had had a big fight about her mum's boyfriend.

"You said you liked Dan," I objected. "You said your mum has been so much happier since she's been seeing him."

"She *is*," Sky wept. "But now I'm just in the way."

"Shut up! Of course you're not."

"I *am*! Before Dan came along, I was Mum's lifeline. You don't know how much she relied on me. I even had to remind her to take her pills. If she was having a bad day, I'd cook for my little brothers—"

"And you were a total superstar!" I interrupted fiercely. "But you're twelve, Sky. You deserve a break. Let Danny Boy take care of her now."

Sky sat up, taking most of my quilt. "It's not just that Mum doesn't *need* me. She doesn't even *like* me."

"Sky—"

"It's true! I remind her of all her worst times. She acts like I'm totally not *there*! I was just trying to make her notice me again," she choked. "But I went a bit too far."

She suddenly clutched at my hand. "She *screamed* in my face, Melanie – she said not to ever bother coming back."

My friend collapsed on to the bed, taking all the quilt this time, and sobbed out: "I felt like there was nobody in the world who cared, Mel. I mean, my dad walks out and now my own mother hates me! What's wrong with this picture? It *has* to be me."

Maybe I was just being swept along with Sky's emotions, but I felt scared for her. I was genuinely afraid she'd do something stupid.

It's hard to be super-positive when you're a tired twelve year old whose teeth are chattering because your friend's got all the quilt. But I started desperately babbling whatever came into my head; telling my friend how amazingly special she was, how she was the girl all the girls in our class secretly wanted to be.

"You've got your whole life ahead of you, Sky," I shivered. "Plus you've got all the Pinks b-backing you up..."

I suddenly realised she'd stopped crying.

Sky groped for my hand. "You missed out the most important thing," she said, hiccupping, "which is you. You're the most wonderful friend I ever had, Melanie, and you'll never leave me, will you?"

I was only twelve. No one expects to die when they're twelve. Plus Sky had just said I was her best mate and I wanted it to be true. So I said something no human should ever say. "Of course I won't leave you, stupid," I whispered.

I only wanted Sky to feel safe so she could go to sleep. And it worked. She snuggled down under the quilt, still clutching my hand and, worn-out from crying, she finally drifted off...

Of course I won't leave you, stupid...

I could hear my well-meaning words ringing round my head as I half-skated around the icy turning into Sky's street.

In London, there's one hour at night when traffic stops and even the city drunks go totally quiet. Just then it was so quiet, the only sound I could hear was my heart hammering in my ears.

Sky's flat was at the end of a terrace of shabby old-fashioned houses. I picked my way down steps slippery with ice and shimmered in through the front door into the Nolans' basement flat.

I wished Brice had given me his scarf as well. It was colder inside the Nolans' place than it was out in the street.

The heating's off, I told myself. *It's the middle of the night, Mel.*

The flat was absolutely silent. When the fridge switched itself on with a sudden judder, I jumped with fright.

Angels can tell a lot from the vibes which collect in human homes. Karmen's home had a super-intense family vibe. Walking into the Jackson's flat felt like walking into some dreary war zone.

Sky's home was an icy blank. I started along the hall, checking in all the rooms, one by one. Kitchen empty. Sitting room empty.

The blind was up in Mrs Nolan's room. Stark-white streetlight flooded in, showing an empty double bed made up with a pristine white quilt. Instead of a depressing clutter of pill bottles, the bedside table had a cute photo of Sky's mum with Dan and two smiling little boys.

The little boys' room was empty too.

They'd obviously all gone to Dan's for the weekend, but I felt I should just check in Sky's room, as I was here.

The Nolan's hall was like an L-shape. Sky's room was around the bend. Her door had been left closed. A handwritten sign said KEEP OUT BRATS OR DIE!!

I shimmered through to the other side and yelled with shock.

My mate was in here all by herself!

She was all huddled up on her bed in an old dressing gown, listening to music through some earphones. She'd got woolly bed socks on, pulled right up to her knees, but she still looked blue with cold. I thought she looked much too thin.

Even if I'd been human I don't think I'd have tried to touch her. It was like she wasn't really here – just waiting. Even Sky's room literally felt like a waiting room. Her pop posters and girly bric-a-brac, precious mementoes of the Pinks, heart-shaped cushions and mad photo booth pics – all had gone, leaving cold empty space.

On the wardrobe door, which Sky used as an overflow for her huge photo collection, just one pic was left. It showed Sky at the London Eye. Sky by herself.

I was numb. I remembered that cool hair-flick. *Sky Nolan, the independent operator.* Sky was always the most ruthless Pink, but I never had her down as a person who'd just cut you out of her life without a backward glance.

"Look closer," said my inner angel.

Goose bumps came up on my arms.

I'd forgotten a basic cosmic law which Mr Allbright made us learn in my first term. You can't destroy energy.

You can't destroy *anything* which is real. And the hyperactive energy of four nutty twelve year olds on the loose – that's real. Sky might look like she was totally alone, but the energies of those other laughing girls still fizzed and sparkled all around her.

I loved those mischievous sparkles; I loved that you could still tell we had our arms around Sky.

A tiny spark of hope lit inside my heart. If you couldn't destroy energy, maybe you couldn't delete a true friendship from the Universe?

I sat down where I could see her face and tried to keep my voice steady. "Sky, don't die of shock. It's me! It's Mel! I've come back." I felt my voice go husky. "Babe, I'm so *so* sorry I didn't get to say goodbye."

Sky ejected the CD and put in a new one.

I told myself she wasn't blanking me on purpose and ploughed on, explaining that I was going to be in town for a few days, so if Sky had any problems I'd be happy to help, but I could feel all this hot embarrassment building up inside.

"I don't know what to say," I told Helix.

"You're fine," she said warmly. "Just talk normally."

I wasn't sure there was a *normal* way to tell someone their dead friend had come back as an angel.

Sky was busy skipping through tracks. I wondered what music she was into now and if I'd like it.

Hitching closer to my unresponsive friend, I tried again. "This isn't just a friendly visit, Sky. I'm here because the Agency – the guys who run the Universe basically – think you're in trouble. They didn't say what kind – they prefer us to figure stuff out for ourselves, but Jax is obviously spinning out of control. And what *is* going on with Karms? Why is she so fixated on this show—"

My friend practically tore off her headphones.

"I am so SICK of that girl and her poxy musical!" she burst out. "Does she think you'll be *watching* them from the clouds?"

It was almost like she was answering me, even though she didn't know I was in the room. Sky got off the bed in a rush and went to the window. She gave a scared laugh. "Great, now you're talking to yourself, Sky."

I rushed across the room. "Sky, listen to me! You're not talking to yourself and I'm not in the clouds, babe – I'm standing right behind you. Can you feel those teeny angel tingles? That's *me*!"

I'd just made things worse. Sky started flapping her hands, like a desperate fanning gesture. "This is SO sick," she said in a kind of moan. "When you're dead you're dead. This is just in your head, Sky."

"Weren't you listening, fool?" I said lovingly. "I'm not a spook! I'm an angel. At least I will be, in about sixty thousand years, when I've—!"

Sky gasped and spun round. "Mel?"

There was pure shock on her face, but there was joy too, I swear; if we could have sat down and talked then, I truly believe things could have been different.

The very next second, a hideous ring tone shattered the silence.

It literally made me see spots in front of my eyes. I was close to throwing up when Sky snatched up her mobile.

I felt our fragile connection snap like a thread. Only one thing makes a girl look like that, and that's a boy.

"Yeah, you've got mine," Sky bubbled. "We must have swapped phones by mistake! They've all gone to Brighton. Yeah, in *this* weather! No, and I wouldn't have gone if she had. Shut UP, you pig! I'm a big girl now, you know!"

Sky was lying on her bed now, acting kittenish. She suddenly creased up laughing. "I'll make you pay for that! So are you coming to pick me up?" I heard her voice falter. "OK, well, I can probably find a cab. Yeah, about ten minutes."

I watched numbly as she rushed round like a human whirlwind, dragging on her little top and skirt, pulling on high stretchy boots, putting in her hoop earrings.

Was this mystery boy's call what my friend had been waiting for? Because there was no resemblance to the blank listless girl of five minutes ago. Grabbing her faux fur jacket, Sky slammed out of the flat.

I beamed myself after her, but Helix told me not to follow her any further.

"This is Park Hall, Helix! Something bad could happen."

"Something bad *has* happened." Helix seemed incredibly sad.

"You don't get it, this is what human girls do! This is *normal* behaviour on my planet. Human girls get boyfriends and fall in love, and suddenly nothing else matters."

"Sweetie, what happened in there is *so* not normal."

"Helix, when it comes to cosmic stuff, I'm happy to take your advice, but this is *my* world, OK, and I think I know it just a *leetle* bit better than you do!"

I was talking out of my angel rear-end. I didn't understand *anything* that had happened since I got here. At least Jax and Karms were still just recognisable as my friends, but as I watched Sky hurrying away into the dark, I felt like I didn't know her at all.

The old Sky had big dreams. She'd seen what happened to girls in Park Hall and she wanted better. No way would she humiliate herself for some boy.

The snow was turning into sleet. I huddled inside Brice's jacket. Something dark was hovering at the edges of my mind, and it was taking a lot of effort to shut it out.

Chapter Nine

As it turned out I was just about to get a lift.

Nearby windows started to rattle in their frames as an Agency motorbike roared up. The rider took off his helmet and I saw dark spiky hair with blond flashes.

"Good, you're still here," Brice grinned. "Hop on and I'll take you back."

I was so upset I had to take it out on somebody.

"I'm a trainee *agent*, Brice. I don't *need* someone following me around like my big brother. I *told* you I'd do this by myself."

"And I respected your wishes, darling! But Jools was worried we forgot to tell you the security code. She didn't want you to be locked out."

"You use your tags – she showed me."

He looked sheepish: "The others were concerned, all right? They didn't think you should be out alone on your first night back. Anyway, can you imagine what Lola would do to me if anything happened?"

"True," I giggled. "You'd have to leave Heaven."

"At least!" he grinned.

Brice tossed me a helmet. He seemed uneasy now, as if he was wondering whether to tell me something. He took a breath. "Actually, before we go back, there's something I want to show you."

"O-kay," I said wearily. "I'm an angel. I don't need to sleep." That's the theory; though personally sleep is one human habit I'm in no hurry to give up.

My hands were so cold it was hard to fasten my helmet. This was my first time on any kind of motorbike. I nervously clambered on.

Brice gunned the engine. Next minute I was scorching through the sleeping city on a celestial motorbike, with my arms wrapped round a Dark angel. I know!

We were travelling at such supersonic speeds, my old neighbourhood was mostly just a blur. Eventually I gave up even *trying* to figure out where I was. Privately, I longed to be tucked up with a milky drink and a hot water bottle.

Several hair-raising minutes later, Brice brought the bike to a halt by the battered Bell Meadow street sign. After he'd helped me off the bike, he just stood beside the sign, blowing on his cold hands, apparently waiting for me to figure something out.

"What did you want to show me again?" I asked through numb lips. I was desperate to speed things up, so we could get back in the warm.

"The *school*, darling, the school," he said wearily.

"I've seen my school, thanks," I flashed. "I *went* to this hellhole, remember!"

Brice grabbed my shoulders, turning me forcibly until I was facing our school annexe with its tacky bridge.

"What is *that*?" I said hoarsely. I forgot all about being cold. I actually took off my helmet, as if that would help the vision go away.

Disturbing lights and shadows flitted to and fro across the bridge between the annexe and the main school. I felt like I was seeing *two* buildings mixed up together: my grim real-life comprehensive and something ghostly, alien and *wrong*.

There was nothing human on that bridge, yet I could hear childlike voices floating from the school;

children's voices spookily remixed by the Powers of Darkness.

Other spine-chilling noises drifted out. I don't know if music has an opposite? It was like they'd got the evil building contractors in and they were listening to Hell FM.

"But how—?" I couldn't seem to get my head around it.

"Your school seems to have sprung a cosmic leak," he said bluntly. It sounded ordinary how Brice phrased it – a minor plumbing problem.

I tried to swallow. "The kids can't see this, can they?"

"Not yet."

"Not yet? This is going to get *worse*!"

But Brice didn't reply and I was too scared to ask again.

For a few moments we watched the eerie lights coming and going across the bridge.

What were they *doing* in there?

And how must those vibes be affecting Park Hall's kids? They had to try to study inside that horror five days a week. They had to get good grades and figure out what they wanted to be when they grew up.

"Did it just, you know, *happen?*" I gulped.

Brice had jammed his hands under his armpits, trying to thaw them out. "We still haven't cracked that one. Maybe the PODS thought it would be interesting to open a crack in human reality."

"Brice! That must be how the hellhound got in!"

"There's not just one, darling," he sighed.

My heart gave a little bump. "How many then?"

He shook his head.

The thought of unknown numbers of hell beasts roaming the corridors just curdled my blood.

My mind flashed back to my premonition when I first arrived – that my two worlds were just about to collide. But I could never have imagined...

Suddenly I couldn't breathe. "Brice, Omigosh – if hell dogs are getting *out* of the Hell dimensions—"

I saw he'd been waiting for me to figure this out.

"*That's* our worry," he said quietly.

I swallowed. "No, that would never – that can't be right."

"It isn't *right*, angel girl. But if we don't find a way to stop it, these kids will find themselves wandering out of their school into..." his voice tailed off.

"Brice, you're freaking me out! Into *what?*"

His expression was unreadable. "Another school, angel girl. Just not school as you know it."

I thought I might be sick. *I went to this hellhole remember!* My thoughtless remark had boomeranged back like a hex. Park Hall Community High School was now officially twinned with a school from Hell.

Chapter Ten

By the time I finally crawled under the covers, I was too upset to do more than doze. I'd crash asleep, then almost instantly shoot bolt upright, my heart racing. No bad dreams, no scary flashes of girl fights or hell schools – just unbelievable horror, mixed with a weird haunting guilt. Like I'd done something so bad it could never be put right.

After a while I heard Jools tiptoeing around in the dark.

I raised myself groggily. "More fights?"

"Off to do the dawn vibes," she whispered. "Go back to sleep."

I sat up. "No, I'd like to come if that's OK."

I hadn't a clue what 'dawn vibes' were, but I had the feeling they'd do me good. I jumped into some jeans and Jools lent me a warm top, plus her roommate's parka, so dawn vibes obviously happened out of doors.

Outside, it was totally pitch black.

"Are you sure this is dawn?" I asked doubtfully.

Jools quickly checked her watch. "No, but it will be in exactly ten minutes!" She grabbed my hand. "Hold on tight!"

"But where are we—?"

The Universe went unexpectedly rippley. When it finally firmed up again we were on snowy parkland high above London.

City lights sparkled below us like scattered jewellery. From here you could see the night was starting to fade. My eyes could just make out vague shapes of tower blocks.

I'd never been on Hampstead Heath this early. It seemed just like I remembered from family outings – except for the angels.

There were hundreds and thousands of them, and more were beaming down every minute.

Like any normal crowd of Londoners, the earth angels came from different age groups, and every walk of life. Some chatted quietly to their friends, others just waited peacefully for the dawn vibes to begin.

It was like a beautiful, but v. surreal, painting: *Angels on Hampstead Heath.*

"Does this happen every day?" I breathed.

"And at sunset," Jools said. "Dawn and dusk are the optimum times to send vibes to the planet."

I made a mental note to incorporate the word 'optimum' into my vocabulary first chance I got.

"So is Hampstead Heath the local energy hot spot?"

I was half joking, but Jools said seriously, "It's *one* of the hot spots, yeah. London has about seven. This is my favourite though."

The idea of *seven* well-known London landmarks filling up with angels twice a day sent me reeling.

When you take a time trip to ancient Rome or whatever, you expect the odd cosmic surprise. But this was *my* time, and I felt like I was having to run to catch up!

"So why do you do dawn vibes again?" I asked.

A young EA in torn trainers joined in our conversation. "I can't speak for the other EAs," she smiled, "but when you work with street kids twenty-four-seven like I do, you almost forget you're in the bizz. Some days I'm the only earth angel at King's Cross. The vibes remind me that

I'm not alone – that I'm connected to every earth angel in this city—"

She suddenly dropped her voice.

"We're starting!" she whispered.

I didn't need anyone to tell me the vibes had begun.

As the first streaks of dawn appeared in the sky, there was this incredible hush, then I heard very faint and unbearably lovely musical chords which seemed to come from out of thin air. Before today I'd never heard those sounds outside of Heaven. Then I noticed how each tiny blade of grass was starting to shimmer and I thought, ohh, but this *is* Heaven! In a few minutes it'll go back to being grim, grimy London, but just now it's Heaven!

My senses were more sensitive since the upgrade. I could actually *see* unearthly colours streaming from the centres of our palms, and whooshing dramatically into Earth's atmosphere. Then zillions upon zillions of tiny gold stars rained back down.

Go vibes, I willed them silently. Humans *really* need you.

I totally understood now why that girl came here on her day off.

At last only a sprinkling of gold stars was left to drift slowly back to Earth. Winter birds twittered all around us. The sun was hidden behind woolly grey clouds, but London skies are almost always grey, and you could see streaks of other, softer colours, mixed in.

"Look at you," Jools exclaimed. "You're all pretty and glowy!"

"I was thinking the same thing about you," I said shyly. "That was amazing, Jools. I'm going to remember it for ever." I gave her a quick hug. "I'll catch up with you later, yeah?"

That's one big thing about dawn vibes. They totally make you know what you should do next.

Chapter Eleven

I'd seen this sitting room so many times in my dreams. Not the bad dreams – my sad, homesick dreams.

In my dreams my mum was always asleep on the sofa, just like now, and, like in the dreams, I wasn't able to go to her straight away.

I softly prowled around my mum's flat, letting myself know I was really here. At first it seemed almost like there were three Mels in the room – the human girl I used to be, the dream Mel in her PJs and the angel girl in her borrowed parka. But gradually it sank in that this visit wasn't a dream or just a memory, but for real.

That vibe – that sweet, homey vibe – was just the same.

There were hyacinths in a bowl on a small table. There's something about the smell of hyacinths that gives me a sad-happy ache inside. Mum had forgotten to take the price sticker off the bowl: special offer, £2.99.

You don't often smell flowers in a dream, you probably don't notice price stickers and you definitely don't see your little sister's half-finished dress hanging off your mum's sewing machine, with the tacking threads dangling down.

My mum had fallen asleep in a really awkward position; she was going to get a bad crick in her neck if she didn't wake up soon. She'd probably been waiting up for my step-dad. Des fixes pumps: those totally massive pumps they use in power stations and sewage plants. I'm telling you, if one of those breaks down, you'd better hope Des gets to you fast!

I was gradually tiptoeing closer to my mum. Finally I dared to crouch down beside the sofa. As an angel, I love watching humans sleep. Their daytime disguises fall away and you actually see who they really are; but for the first time I felt like I was intruding.

There was something in my mum's face that I felt like I wasn't supposed to see: a sadness so deep, it had marked her for ever. Even when she was old it would be there.

Next to the TV was a picture of me in a twirly silver frame. I'd seen this photo plenty of times in my dreams, but until now I'd never seen it in real life. Des must have taken it on my thirteenth birthday.

"Weird," I whispered.

Without realising it, I was stroking my mum's face, softly smoothing out her new worry lines. For the first time I noticed silver hairs glinting among her trendy new highlights and I felt this terrible pang. She was my mum. Mums are supposed to stay the same for ever.

Our old video machine was flashing zeros. Mum and Des never could get the hang of VCRs.

"You want to get a DVD player," I told my mum. "You want to move with the times, girl."

Then eighteen months of tears just welled up, and I put my head down on the sofa and howled. "Oh, Mum I've missed you—" I gave up even trying to put so much pain into words, and just cried and cried.

After a few minutes, I covered my face with my hands. "I'm not supposed to be doing this! This was supposed to be beautiful, like in movies!"

I quickly wiped my eyes. "I had it all planned out – no, I did! I was going to be incredibly calm and bathed in light and you'd be like, totally awed but at the same time really *really* happy to know I'd gone to a better place. And I *have*, Mum," I sobbed out. "I have such a beautiful life – this is just so much harder than I ever..."

I had to stop to take deep breaths.

"Guess I just wanted to impress you, huh?" I giggled tearily. "Guess I'm not as angelic as I thought!"

I blew my nose. After a while I said, "I see Des got round to repainting the flat. He did a good job."

I didn't care if I was wittering. Why would you need to impress your mum? It was enough to be with her, smelling hyacinths and nattering about nothing. Finally I felt able to leave her, but only because I knew I'd be coming back. I tiptoed into the room I used to share with my little sister.

This room too had been freshly repainted. Our old twin beds had gone. Jade was asleep in one of those smart pine cabin beds with built-in shelves and whatever underneath. Her curtains and bed covers were in pastel pink with a cute fairy motif.

I understood why they did it. It must have been painful for them coming into this room every day, seeing that empty bed. Humans don't live for ever. They have to find a way to move on.

Climbing stealthily up the short ladder, I softly lay down on my side next to Jade, so I could look into her face.

"Hi, Fluffyhead," I whispered. "I bet you feel like the princess of Park Hall in this bed, yeah? I love the fairies. Did Mum let you choose the pattern by yourself?"

With her elfin eyelids and little pointy face, Jade looked a lot like a fairy herself. She'd grown in the eighteen months I'd been gone. She was going to be a daddy-longlegs like her sister. Yet to me she seemed touchingly small and vulnerable.

Her limp little hand still smelled of warm wax crayons like I remembered. I stroked it softly. "I can't stay now, Jadie, but I'll be around for a few days, so I'll come and see you again, I promise." I plonked an angel kiss on her cheek. "Love you!"

"Love you, Mel," Jade murmured in her sleep.

I gasped. I was so shocked, I beamed myself down into the street without even trying, and just started walking.

A guy was trying to start his rusty old banger. Across the road, the Minimart was open. A van was delivering bread.

I walked past everything in a daze.

First Sky, now Jade!

Two humans had heard me talking. OK, Jade was my sister, so there was a strong link, but Sky was wearing headphones!!

Suddenly it was like I'd been struck by lightning. I literally looked up at the sky, as if this amazing revelation had been dropped from a passing plane!

"So that's why the Agency couldn't send me till I'd had my birthday," I breathed. "Omigosh, I have to tell Lollie!"

I fumbled in the pockets of my parka and called her on my dinky Agency mobile. There was a click and a hiss and I Lola's recorded message. "Talk to the phonhearde, *carita*, cos the face ain't home. Please leave a message after the tone. BEEP!!"

"Lollie!" I shouted into my phone. "I'm outside my old flats! I know! Listen, I'm going to road-test our survival guide for real. That's my *mission*, Lollie! Michael said I'd figure out what I had to do and now

I have! I'm going to teach my mates every cosmic survival technique in our book!"

When I got back to the house, I went to fetch myself some cereal and came back humming. I found Brice and Jools in the TV room.

"You're perky, angel girl," Brice commented. "You were in the depths of despair last night."

"I feel great!" I bubbled. "I've figured out why Michael sent me. I was just walking along and – I totally saw what I have to do!"

"Let me guess!" he said in a sarky tone. "You're going to flit between your mates, beaming pretty vibes, until all of a sudden they rush to one another's homes, kiss and make up. And little Mel goes back to Heaven tired but happy because her work on Earth is done."

I felt like he'd hit me. For a moment I just stared in shock, then I just saw red. "Ooh, silly me, wanting to help my friends!" I flashed. "Brice, those girls are in *bits*!"

"So?" he said coldly. "You're an angel, not their agony aunt."

"And you're a heartless *pig*!"

"At least I'm not living in La-la land! I wish you'd

at least stop and *think*, darling, before you flit off to play good fairy."

"Brice, what the sassafras is there to think about! Michael *sent* me to help my friends!"

He got that pinched look he gets when he's upset. "You're absolutely sure about that? There couldn't *possibly* be any more to your mission than saving your precious girls?"

He finally noticed Jools frantically shaking her head and abruptly walked out of the room. Jools went after him and I heard them arguing in low voices.

I was trembling from Brice's attack. *This is so typical of that boy*, I thought shakily. You just decide you can trust him then he publicly humiliates you. OK, so his good-fairy crack had come a teeny bit too close, but did he have to be so *mean*.

I decided I wasn't going to talk to Brice again, *ever*.

When it seemed like the coast was clear, I ran up to get my bag.

On my way upstairs, I glimpsed Delphine watching the TV monitors with a glazed expression, but as I hurtled back down, I saw the door had been closed.

I heard Jools' worried voice.

"How do you tell someone something like that?"

"You can't," Delphine murmured sympathetically. "I'm sure you're doing the right thing."

I didn't like to barge in on a private EA chat, so I left without saying anything to anyone.

Outside it was sleeting again, and I quickly pulled up my furry parka hood. *I don't care* what *that creep thinks, I told myself, shivering. I feel really privileged to be on such an unusual and exciting mission.* And I beamed myself smoothly through space.

Chapter Twelve

In order of urgency, my official worry list now read:

1. Sky Nolan
2. Eve Jackson
3. Karmen Patel

However, Sky wouldn't be back home for hours yet, so rather than twiddling my little angel thumbs I'd decided to start with Jax.

I shimmered into her room feeling v. slick and professional.

My mate was still sleeping deeply, one arm dangling off the bed. Her fingertips had raw places where she bit her nails.

I was pleased I'd got here before she woke up. Sleeping humans are *way* more open to angelic suggestion.

I sat down beside her, trying not to notice the grubby sheets. Don't get the impression Jax was a slutty person. When I knew her, she was the cleanest girl I knew. Jax washed her hair *every* day, and if she ate something at school, she'd have to brush her teeth immediately afterwards. I'm not sure where she got that habit. It definitely wasn't her parents.

Jax was the youngest Jackson and the only girl. She reckoned that after four trouble-making boys, her parents just lost interest. They gave her a sweet name – Eve. After that, Jax was basically on her own. I think she did a great job of bringing herself up. OK, there was the shoplifting, but if your mum and dad don't teach you right from wrong, you're not going to learn *that* from a teen magazine, are you?

Jax's eyes were moving under her lids. She was dreaming.

I smiled to myself. The conditions for my friend's first angel lesson were almost perfect. Later in the day something might just go 'click' and she'd remember her mad dream where her dead friend was in her room, wearing pink suede boots and claiming to be an angel.

"Jax? It's me, Mel. The first thing I want to say is I'm not a scary spook – though hopefully you can tell the difference from the vibes!"

I was watching her face alert for the tiniest response.

"I'm an angel, Jax! Kind of a surprise, yeah? Don't ask why they picked me, because I have NO idea! Listen, I'll probably be around for a few days and I've just had this really cool idea."

I shifted a little closer to Jax.

"Tell you how it started – I was actually wishing you guys could all come back with me and be angels just for a day. I know it's just a fantasy, but it got me thinking. I have such a beautiful life, Jax! I live in this huge vibey city, and I'm going to this cool angel school! I went into pure shock, though, when they first told me! I'm like, 'I'm *dead* and I have to go to school!'"

Jax's mouth quirked up at the corners. My heart gave a little skip. Could she possibly be smiling at my joke?

I was stroking her hand, willing her to hear my voice. "You might actually *like* going to school in Heaven! When you're training to be an angel, you know you're part of something HUGE, and it makes you feel so proud, Jax. I never felt like that before, and I want to share it with you, girl!"

Did I just imagine it, or did my friend give a soft little sigh?

"So then I'm like, OK, maybe your mates can't go to angel high school, Melanie, but what's to stop you taking the angel school to *them*? Yeah, I *know*! Creative thinking or what! I'm not talking scary advanced stuff, just basic cosmic laws, simple techniques for keeping yourself safe and whatever? You'd be like, an *undercover* angel! Would you be up for that?"

I heard another soft sigh. I took that as a yes, and settled myself into a calm yoga sitting pose. I was about to teach my first official angel lesson.

"Listen carefully now, babe, because I'm going to tell you something that will blow you away. You're magic, Jax!"

If Jax remembered just this one thing, it would change her life.

I took a deep breath. "And it's not just you, girl. *Everyone's* born magic, even that stinky old man who used to come into Costcutter. He doesn't look so magic now, but that's because he's got something called 'cosmic amnesia'..."

I told Jax that she must never think she was alone – that she had a huge celestial organisation watching out for her – and I dropped a tiny hint about the PODS for her to think about when she was awake.

When I'd given my mate as much cosmic info as I thought she could absorb for one day, I slung my bag over my shoulder.

"You're magic, Jax," I repeated softly. "Never forget that, yeah?"

I checked my watch. Time to shoot off to Karmen's.

On my way out, I noticed the cactus.

Maybe it had just been pretending to be dead, or maybe it was just the right time for it to come back to life? I don't really know about cactuses. All I know is that *this* cactus had a tiny, shocking-pink flower shyly blooming from its withered little stump.

Karmen's bedroom smelled of hot clean hair. She was in front of the mirror using her hair straighteners. There was like, *one* tiny kink in her hair and she was stressing like you would not believe.

This morning my friend was looking extra grown-up and serious, in a fabulous *shalwar kamiz* sparkling with gold threads. Karms is actually more of a cool-casuals girl, so I guessed her parents were dragging her off to the rellies later.

Checking her straighteners were switched off, Karmen ran back to the mirror and started yanking crossly at her hair.

"Karmen Asha Patel," I said sternly. "You look totally luminous, so stop stressing!"

She stopped! She actually walked away from the mirror!! I hadn't even got started yet!!

Maybe it was just a coincidence though, because Karmen immediately started burrowing madly in her wardrobe, until she located a pair of pretty sandals which would match her outfit.

"Karms," I said in the same firm voice. "Just chill, OK?"

And again she stopped, only this time there was something in her eyes that hadn't been there before.

"Babe?" I said excitedly. "Can you hear me? It's Mel. I'm an angel, Karms. I know! I hardly believe it myself, but it's true."

Karmen's eyes went all wistful. Suddenly she did a strange, not to say slightly creepy, thing. She walked up to the photo with its little scented candle and talked to it!

"I hope you'd be proud of me, Mel," she whispered. "I really do."

"Karms, I'm *humongously* proud of you," I said warmly, "but I'm actually right behind you, and I'm only in town a few days and we've got a LOT of ground to cover. You see... EEK," I squeaked.

Karmen had walked right through me on her way to the karaoke machine. Her room filled with cheesy music and to my dismay Karmen started belting out one of the big numbers from GREASE.

Ever tried teaching cosmic survival to someone who's yelling, "You're the One that I Want" at the top of her lungs?

Luckily I soon saw the funny side. I imagined Reubs and Lola howling as I described my frustrated attempt to pass on angel skills to a caterwauling Karmen. Knowing Reubs, he wouldn't see a problem! He'd be like, "Why didn't you just go with the flow, angel girl?"

Yeah, angel girl, I thought. *Just go with the flow!*

So I sang along!

It was fun! I can't sing for peanuts, but I really got into it. Halfway through the number, Karms and I lost all our inhibitions and launched into a wild dance routine. I can't swear to it, but I thought I saw her throw in some cheeky Bollywood moves.

When the music finished, we both had to get our breath back.

"Woo, that was fun! Almost like old times!" I panted. "Except obviously I was visible then!"

Omigosh, I thought. *Look at you, girl.*

All the strain had left her face. She was glowing from dancing and laughing in that way you do when you've been kidding around.

Then her eyes went wistful again. "Oh, Melanie, I hope they let you be one in Heaven," she said softly.

She was looking past me to our London Eye photo, but it was a v. shivery moment. It was like, Karmen didn't *absolutely* know I was here, but she *kind* of did.

And be one *what* in Heaven?

"Karms—" I started.

"Time to go, *beti*!" her dad sang from the hall.

I'd been at Karmen's house exactly twenty minutes!

I thought Reuben would be *très* proud of me for managing to stay so chilled. What did it matter if my friend and I connected during a cheesy song and dance routine, so long as we connected? And we had. I still had the goose bumps to prove it.

Two down, one to go, I thought, shimmering out into the street.

In case Sky was still with lover boy, I went the long way round, strolling past shops and cafes. I think the dawn vibes were still fizzing in my veins, because I was genuinely loving being out in my old community. I started feeling like a bona fide local angel, bopping along in my borrowed parka, so I thought it was time I behaved like one.

I started sending vibes to anyone who looked like they needed it (yeah, yeah, so maybe a couple of times I sent them to really fit boys – I'm an angel, babe, not a saint!!).

Soon angel vibes were raining down everywhere. I'm talking *serious* showers of gold sparkles. Little kids were smiling. Old married couples were holding hands. Park Hall was literally becoming a better place!

I felt that special glow inside my chest. Helix wanted a word.

"Isn't this just pure magic!" I bubbled.

"The best magic there is, sweetie. Not sure you should draw this much attention to yourself though. Did you forget angels aren't the only beings who see vibes?"

"Oops," I said guiltily. "Sorry, I'll stop. It was *très* cool though."

It was late afternoon by the time I picked my way down the basement steps to the Nolans' flat. They were glassy with ice, though it had mostly melted everywhere else.

I could hear a radio DJ talking through the door.

I found Sky in the kitchen whizzing up a diet shake.

"Hiya," I said, when she'd eventually switched off the blender. Sky carefully poured her shake into a glass and stood at the counter, gulping it down. My mate was dressed for comfort now, in trackie bottoms and a hoody she must have worn for decorating; you could see teeny streaks and splodges of paint.

"Babe?" I tried again.

The microwave dinged. Sky had been microwaving some popcorn. She took her snack to the table. An old R&B number came on. Sky moved her body while she munched, but from her eyes you knew she was back with the boyfriend, or fantasising how it would be next time.

"See you're back on the Popcorn Diet," I commented. "Not that you need to lose weight. You're too skinny, girl!"

My friend was alternating mouthfuls of popcorn with gulps of diet shake. I wondered if she could taste them.

I softly put my hand over hers, the first time I'd touched her. "Where are you, Sky?" I whispered. "You heard me last night."

She started picking at a miniscule speck of paint on her sleeve.

"Just tell her what's in your heart," Helix suggested. "Isn't that what real friends do? Tell each other the truth?"

I realised she was right. Now the Pinks had split up, Sky didn't have a single mate who could give her a reality check.

I took a shaky breath. "Babe, I'm sure you think you're in love, but I'm your friend, OK, plus I'm an angel, and I'm telling you he's playing with you, girl! He doesn't care about you! No decent boy would make you run around these streets in the middle of the night."

I could hear my voice getting husky.

"I was *so* scared for you, last night, Sky. I was scared for all you guys. I didn't think I could *be* more scared until I saw that—"

I just caught myself before I started to describe

the eerie comings and goings in the school annexe. This flash of fear wasn't anything I could put into words, but it had to do with that worryingly passive vibe my friend was putting out. I felt like even *mentioning* the Dark Powers just then could make them pop up right there in the Nolans' kitchen. How Sky was now left wide open to any dark vibe that blew in off the street.

So many people in her life had let her down, and now she seemed lost – she'd forgotten who she was and had just given up on herself.

"Everyone leaves me," she'd sobbed out that night.

You'd think that wouldn't you, if your dad walks out and your so-called mother sees nothing wrong with abandoning you for an entire weekend in a dangerous city?

You left her too, Melanie, whispered the dark angels who'd come to live at the back of my mind. I tuned them out, quick as a flash. I was here *now* wasn't I? And unlike those other people who'd disappointed Sky, I was going to take proper care of my friend; more importantly, I was going to teach her how to take care of herself.

I didn't care what Brice, Helix or *anyone* said. My

first task was to help my friend get back her old feisty self-confidence.

I decided to start by just beaming positivity.

"You're such a star, Sky," I said in my warmest, most upbeat voice. "Do you know that? All you need is some really basic cosmic info, then you'll be like, *untouchable*. A few minutes a day, that's all it'll take, but you'll be amazed at the results."

Yeah, I know it sounded like I was recommending heavenly beauty products, but with Sky how she was, it could be dangerous to get into anything too heavy. I was giving her like the fuzzy pink version of Cosmic Survival for Humans – Lesson 1.

With Sky I basically stressed over and over that she wasn't alone. "It's soo simple! But, once you've grasped this one basic fact, I swear, your whole Universe will be like, *transformed*."

Sky abruptly brushed past me on her way out of the kitchen.

Still talking, I followed her into the sitting room, where she'd left the gas fire full on. She crouched down, holding out blue-tinged hands to the flames.

For all the response I was getting, she might have had her earphones in. I felt like she could, *technically*, hear me, but some deeply suspicious part of Sky was deleting my words as fast as I put them out.

But even when my mate turned on the TV and started flicking through channels, I refused to be depressed.

Sky had taken a lot of knocks. You couldn't expect her to turn into a PODS-kicking undercover angel in just one lesson!

She finally settled for an MTV channel. An old feel-good music video came on. "Where is the Love?" by the Black Eyed Peas.

"That is *just* the kind of thing I've been talking about," I said in my new, upbeat voice. "Here's you thinking you're all alone in the Universe, and you get this *major* sign, don't you see! You know why that happens, babe? It's because everything is *totally* connected! That's why, if we ask the Universe for—"

"You should stop now," Helix interrupted.

"But I haven't told her about the cosmic strings—"

"Tell her tomorrow," said Helix gently. "You're getting tired."

Until she pointed it out, I hadn't noticed how weird I was feeling: drained and muzzy. Teaching angel skills to humans who aren't listening uses more energy than you'd think. I badly needed to rest, but I felt bad about leaving Sky alone again.

"You're going to be OK, sweetie," I told her one last time. "One day you'll wake up and you'll absolutely know why you're here and who you are. It's not your fault you've got cosmic amnesia. Lola—"

"Enough!" insisted Helix.

"You're *magic*, Sky," I told my friend stubbornly, as I slung my Agency bag over my shoulder. "Deep *deep* down inside, you're magic."

Back at the Agency house, Jools was pottering in the kitchen.

"Hiya," I said, in a feeble little voice.

Jools didn't say a word, just pulled out a chair and made me sit down. Fetching a tiny bottle from the first-aid box, she sent it whizzing across the table. "Two drops," she ordered. "No more than that or it'll blow your head off!"

I dripped exactly two drops cautiously on my tongue.

"Woo!" I shook myself like a puppy. "That feels *better*!"

"Angel drops!" grinned Jools. "An Earth Angel's best friend, closely followed by chocolate! Speaking of which—"

Jools quickly washed out two mugs and made us both some hot chocolate. It was from a packet but I didn't care; it felt *sooo* good to be taken care of.

"Where's Brice?" I asked cautiously.

"He... do you know, I'm actually not sure," she smiled. "But he left you a note."

Jools handed me a torn piece of paper. I unfolded it cautiously. No 'Dear Mel'. No signature. Just seven words in Brice's thick black scrawl.

Sorry I called you a good fairy.

Chapter Thirteen

I woke on Sunday morning to find my inner angel had switched my plans in the night. Instead of giving Sky her intensive coaching session on cosmic string theory, Helix had decided I was spending my day in a school with an inter-dimensional leak, watching Karmen's rehearsal.

When I emerged from the bathroom, washed and dressed, I was surprised to see Jools sitting on the stairs in her PJs.

She took a breath. "Mel, everyone's so impressed with what you're doing for your friends – if it's OK, we'd like to help."

I was so grateful I didn't know whether to kiss her or cry. The EAs were already working all around the clock, yet they were willing to stretch to give my friends the help they needed.

"You realise this is going to be *très* scary?" I called after Jools, as she disappeared into the bathroom.

Jools spun, looking anxious. "You mean the leak?"

I giggled. "I was thinking of Karms singing 'Beauty School Dropout!'"

Jools and I set off walking to my old school, chatting and giggling. Outside the Cosmic Café, Nikos, the owner, was taking off the security grille, ready to open up for Sunday customers. I just couldn't resist.

"Hiya!" I called. "It's Mel, Des's girl!! I'm visiting Earth!"

I saw him smile to himself, as if he were enjoying a private joke, then he calmly disappeared back into the cafe.

I almost fell over. "Did he *hear* me?"

Jools chuckled. "We have *some* humans on our side you know! Nikos is a sweet guy. Really looks out for the local kids."

We'd reached the noisy dual carriageway.

"You never told me how the lessons went?" Jools said, raising her voice above the roar of traffic.

"I think it *kind* of went OK with Jax," I told her.

Then I found myself pouring out my worries about Sky.

"That first night, I *know* she heard me, Jools! Then her boyfriend rang and – bosh! – we're back to square one."

"Any idea who the boyfriend is?" she asked.

"No – and I don't want to," I flashed. "You know what upsets me? None of this would be happening if the Pinks hadn't broken up. We kept each other on track, you know. Now they're all over the place!"

Jools suddenly got busy rearranging her scarf. I had an uneasy feeling she was getting ready to tell me some home truths.

"When you talk about your friends," she said tentatively, "I almost get the feeling you were like, the magic glue that was holding everything together."

I felt a dark rushing in my head, as if all the Dark angels had taken off at once. For a moment I felt actually physically sick. Because if I was the Shocking Pinks' glue and I suddenly wasn't around, that meant, it meant—

Jools quickly put her arm around me. She let me cry for a little while, then I felt her rubbing my back.

"You do know none of this is your fault? You *died*, sweetie! It was out of your control!"

"I just get so scared for them," I choked. "We know the score, Jools, but they have NO idea! I mean, those creeps came out in the cold to watch Jax fight, and yesterday at Sky's—"

Jools made me look at her. "I'm going to tell you something, angel girl," she said fiercely. "No matter what happens to your friends, I want you to *remember* this, OK?"

"OK," I quavered.

"It's going to take time, maybe years, but they *will* come through this, Melanie, and they'll all be stronger for it."

I wasn't actually sure if Jax or Sky had years, the way they were going on. But I felt genuinely comforted. Not just because of the pep talk, but because I realised I'd made a really lovely friend.

We'd crossed the invisible border into the dodgy part of Bell Meadow. A boy in a huge coat barged past, visibly stressing; you could hear him huffing to himself. He went storming through our school gates.

The school looked surprisingly normal by daylight. A burned-out car was smouldering in the loading bay, but of course that's normal for Park Hall.

"Hopefully it won't feel too bad inside today," Jools sighed. "We've sent guys in to do cosmic sweeps, plus we've been pumping in vibes. That *should* slow things down."

"I don't suppose anyone's figured out how to *fix* this leak?" I asked anxiously.

"You know what I woke up thinking?" she asked suddenly. "I thought, *maybe the leak isn't up to us to fix.*"

"You think we need to call in the Big Guys in Suits?"

"Actually just the opposite," she smiled. "This might sound a bit radical, but I think maybe it's down to these kids."

Mr Lupton had told them to be there by half past nine.

When Jools and I walked into the hall at 9.35, just two kids had turned up – Karmen and the stressed boy who'd passed us earlier.

"No one's coming, man," he huffed. "They're all cosy in their beds. Like we'd be if we had any sense," he added darkly.

I didn't think I'd seen him at rehearsal, but something about him seemed familiar. He had unusual eyebrows, black and sort of slanting. If he wasn't so mean and moody, he'd be almost good-looking.

From the way Karmen was pretending not to look at him, she thought so too! "They're coming, Jordie," she insisted. "They *promised.*"

"Because they wanted you out of their *face*!" he flashed.

"Perhaps I'll give them till ten," Mr Lupton said bravely.

At that moment, three extremely disdainful-looking girls strolled in, closely followed by four boys. The boys were all yawning and looking fed up.

After that, nothing. Our drama teacher was still at least ten kids short of an actual musical.

Jools and I had been sitting on the stage, boosting the light levels to discourage any lurking hell critters that got overlooked in the sweep.

"Poor Mr Lupton," I sighed. "He's been trying to get this production off the ground since he started teaching."

Jools pulled a face "Why is he so fixated on this musical?"

"I think maybe he did it in college?"

She rolled her eyes. "*How* many centuries ago?"

"*Jools!*" I giggled.

"Look, he's a lovely guy, but anyone can see he didn't grow up round here. He never had to lie awake listening to police helicopters and emergency sirens stressing up the place! These kids need something they can genuinely relate to." She gestured out into the hall. "Now *that's* their style!"

Two boys were body popping to pass the time. Egged on by shouts from the girls, their moves got steadily slicker and more outrageous.

Jordie suddenly came striding purposefully towards the stage. He vaulted up and grabbed a mike off the stand.

"Check, check," he said experimentally. Jordie shut his eyes and in a surprisingly good voice, belted out, "PRESSURE! The Park Hall youths dem under too much pressure!"

All the kids except Karmen clapped and cheered.

"You *know* that, man, *serious* pressure!" one of the body poppers yelled back.

Jordie started jabbing his fingers at a huge, imaginary audience, as he began to rap. This was nothing unusual. Plenty of white boys at my school thought they could rap. The difference was this boy was good.

Next time I looked the girls had kind of casually drifted up on to the stage. To my surprise they started doing some really chilled street-dancing. They looked just as disdainful, but now it fitted with the ambience.

Jordie had shrugged his coat almost off his shoulders as he prowled around the stage still spouting lyrics. The other boys were calling out, half-mocking, half-genuinely impressed. Even Mr Lupton was smiling and clapping (usually missing the beat, bless him).

By this time the vibe coming off Jordie was just electric. Totally gripped by his performance, I only half-registered a stealthy creak as the door opened just wide enough for a latecomer to slip into the hall.

My heart gave a tiny jump. I'd had a totally mad idea. I turned to Jools. "Wouldn't it be great if Mr Lupton would just drop the musical," I bubbled, "and let the kids put on their own show?"

Jools just lit up. "Melanie that is such a brilliant—!"

She broke off and I saw her eyes go wide with shock. "Is that Jax at the back there?"

It's not surprising Jools was confused. *I* was confused – and she was my friend! This was a totally new version of Eve Jackson. In her soft winter sweater and slouchy velvet jeans, with a knitted beany pulled down over her hair, this girl could have posed for one of those 'celebs off-duty' shots in style zines.

My earth-angel mate pretended to smack me round the head. "'Ooh, I don't *know*, Jools. I think *maybe* my angel lessons went *OK*, Jools.' *Melanie*! She's like a different person!"

I was speechless. I believe in this stuff, I really do, I just hadn't expected it to work so FAST.

Not only had Jax left off her gangster jacket, she'd taken out *every* stud except one. It takes more than a few studs to turn a girl into a gangster of course; what made me know this change was real was the look in her eyes. Just once or twice, in our Shocking Pink days, I'd seen my friend's eyes shine like this.

Jax watched for a while, moving her body slightly to the driving rattatat of Jordie's lyrics, then she made her way to the front of the hall, where Mr Lupton was talking to an increasingly depressed Karmen.

"Hi, girl," Jax greeted her quietly.

"Hi." Karmen didn't even look at her. "Nice of you to come along and say I told you so!"

"Only I didn't," Jax told her quietly. "You did your best, you know. I just think you've all been—" she stopped.

"No, go ahead, stick the knife in," Karmen said in a cold voice. "You know you're dying to!"

Jax took a breath. "I *just* think you've all been barking up the wrong tree. No offence, sir," she said to Mr Lupton, "but your musical sucks, basically."

"I feel forced to agree," he said in a tired voice. "I really think it's time to call it a day."

"We can't give up *now*!" Karmen's voice came out like a despairing wail. "We've got to find a way to make this work!"

"Because of Mel?" Jax said softly.

Karm's chin wobbled, then she hid her face in her hands. "We've got to, we've just *got* to," she sobbed. "It meant so much to her, Jax, but we were so worried about losing our cred, we wouldn't even give it a try, and now Mel's dead!"

I was turning hot and cold.

What made it so much worse is that I wasn't even *that sold* on being a Pink Lady in the first place. But now I was dead, Karms remembered a passing whim as like, my dying *wish*.

My poor friend was putting herself through the wringer, all because – for a whole ten minutes – I'd fancied dressing up in a cute retro jacket so I could flirt with Kelsey Hickman!

Karms was weeping openly now. "I *miss* her, Jax! I miss her and I really miss the Shocking Pinks."

To my horror Jax's eyes filled with tears.

"I miss her too," she gulped.

Jools and I clutched each other's hands in disbelief.

My friends were hugging.

Jax swiped away her tears, trying to pull herself together. "Karms, don't laugh, but when I came in just now I had this mad idea. I know you want to do something for Mel, but why can't it be something she'd be proud of, something classy that we'd *all* be proud of?"

"Like Shakespeare you mean?" Karmen quavered.

Jax gave a tearful laugh. "Haven't you *notice*d what's happening on that stage?"

"One little white boy is not a show, Jax!"

"Girl, wake up! Loads of kids in this school perform in garage bands or whatever."

"You seriously think we can put on a new show in two weeks?"

"Why not?" Mr Lupton chipped in unexpectedly. "As you said yourself, they build gardens in a poxy weekend on TV!"

"But *they* know what they're *doing,*" Karms objected.

"And again, thank you children of Park Hall!" he said humorously.

"I meant we'd be doing this totally from scratch."

"Karms, it will just snowball, girl, trust me! Kids will text their mates and – bosh! – you've got your show!"

The kids on the stage saw something was going on and ambled down into the hall.

"Whassup?" demanded Jordie. "You guys plotting a revolution?"

Jax's eyes glinted. "We're gonna kill Mr Lupton's musical!"

He snorted. "That musical been dead a while, man."

Karmen was shocked. "That's not what you said before, Jordan Hickman!"

Jax grinned. "Because he fancies you rotten, Karms!"

Omigosh, I thought. *No wonder I recognised that face! Stressed Jordie was beautiful Kelsey's younger brother.*

Jax started telling the others about her brainwave for a totally original production. "I'm talking a serious twenty-first century vibe, yeah? But, like, totally positive and uplifting – none of your guns rubbish," she told Jordie fiercely, as if she'd never had a violent thought in her life.

Mr Allbright once told us that when the time is *really* ripe for something to happen, you don't always have to do that much. Everything just unfolds like a wonderful story.

That's exactly how it was with this new show. In less than sixty earth minutes, it flashed from being an angel's daydream to a genuine possibility.

Part-way through Jax's explanation, as she'd predicted, everyone just started texting their mates. In no time would-be performers started rolling up. By 11am, auditions were underway.

Hendrix and Brice turned up in the middle of a cool hip-hop number by a local posse who performed under the name of The Vibe Tribe.

I hadn't seen Brice since our fight, but I'd decided to accept his fairy note as a genuine apology and gave him a friendly smile.

"You guys do realise this hall is buzzing with positive vibes?" he said accusingly.

We hadn't actually noticed, but the air was literally shimmering!

Brice watched the hip-hop kids with a perplexed expression. "I thought Grease was that retro thing with motorbikes?"

We explained about the musical being killed off.

He frowned. "You think they can pull this together in two weeks?"

"With a little cosmic backup," Jools smiled.

"You guys are taking on a lot," I said doubtfully. "You work twenty-four-seven as it is, plus you've got this leak, plus I'd still appreciate some help with my mates."

Jools patted my hand. "And you've got it, hon. But I'm actually wondering if your mates *need* more lessons. Just supporting their show will do wonders for these girls."

But *Sky* isn't in this show, I wanted to say, when Brice said something that blew me away.

"It won't just do wonders for the girls." Brice was trying to play it cool, but even he couldn't keep a glint of hope out of his voice. "These vibes are off the scale, man, and this is the auditions! Imagine an actual show with an audience of proud rellies and well-wishers. The PODS can't stand stuff like that; it's too real – and I should know!" Brice added, flashing me his pantomime baddie smile.

"Are you saying this little show could save the school?" asked Hendrix, amazed.

I felt a whoosh of excitement. "Omigosh, Jools! That's what you meant about it being down to the kids!"

"That was just a hunch, you know," she said softly.

By midday everyone was ready for a break. My mates shared Karmen's lunch while they discussed various artists they'd seen.

After their snack, Jax and Karmen went to freshen up. I was suddenly curious to know what they'd talk about.

I mimed that I'd be back and followed my mates into the skanky cloakroom.

"Could you smell this, like, *perfume*?" I heard Karms say in an awed voice.

Jax shook her head. "More like flowers. What's that pinky bush in your mum's garden?"

"Omigosh, lilacs! You're *right*! After she'd gone I could smell lilacs for *hours*!" Karmen's words were almost tripping over themselves. "Jax, this is *so* incredible. Was it like she was *there* with you, talking?"

"Totally! She said I was magic. She went on about that a LOT."

Karmen gasped. "That's exactly what she said to me!"

"She kept saying I wasn't alone, and when I woke up my dead cactus had a *flower*, Karms! A freaking *shocking-pink* flower!"

"No *way*!" Karmen breathed.

Two girls came in and my friends got busy tidying their hair, continuing their conversation in whispers. I heard Jax hiss, "Then we've got to *make* her talk to us. This is more important than some poxy boy. I mean if Mel came back—?"

"—then Sky totally has to know," Karmen whispered.

I practically floated out of the cloakrooms.

Almost the first thing I'd noticed about Heaven was how the air smells almost exactly, but not quite, like lilacs. Without me knowing, the sweet and magical vibes of Heaven had followed me to Earth!

Suddenly anything seemed possible. Karmen and Jax were determined to make it up with Sky, and we might actually save the school!! It looked like my mission was succeeding beyond my wildest dreams.

Trust Brice to burst my bubble.

"You've got that good fairy look again," He said accusingly when I wafted back into the hall.

"Say what you like, angel boy," I said airily. "But you can't bring me down. Just look around – is this, or is this not, fabulous?"

"Yes, Tinkerbell, it's fabulous and you're fabulous. Just imagine how even more fabulous you'll be when you figure out what your real—" Brice broke off, looking oddly embarrassed.

Jools had joined us. She'd been called out to the children's hospital. A newborn was having trouble adjusting to terrestrial vibes.

"Want to come, Mel?" she offered. "These auditions could go on for hours."

I was suddenly torn. "I'd love to but if I'm not needed here I'd really like to spend some time with my family."

Mum and Des took Jade to the park on Sunday afternoons.

To my secret dismay, Brice asked if he could tag along. Since that Tinkerbell crack, I wasn't keen, but I couldn't really think of a way to say no.

Being Brice, he immediately had to take over. "There's loads of parks in London. I hope you know which one?"

"No, but it's bound to be one of three," I shrugged.

I was wrong.

My family weren't in any of the London parks within easy reach of my old home, and they weren't at home.

It was Brice who figured out where they'd gone.

CHAPTER FOURTEEN

Brice wouldn't say where he was taking me, but I felt cold blank vibes seeping into me, even before we beamed down.

My chest went tight as I watched them trudging stoically along the endless rows of stone crosses and marble angels, looking desperately vulnerable in this bleak open space.

Brice had brought me to the cemetery.

They'd bought bunches of daffodils in sheaths of cellophane. I saw Des wipe his eyes. He put his arms around my mum and I wanted to put my arms around both of them.

This might sound weird, but I was terrified I'd accidentally catch sight of my own headstone.

"Whatever it says, you know that's not you,"

Brice told me with unusual gentleness.

"I don't care, I'm not looking," I told him through stiff lips.

I was looking everywhere *but* my headstone at the winter sky with its criss-crossing vapour trails, at Jade sulkily kicking stones...

"I could read your epitaph to you if you want?" Brice suggested helpfully. "It's not so bad."

I pulled a face. "Does it say I'm sleeping with the angels?"

"Along those lines," he agreed. He flashed a mischievous grin. "Had much sleep lately?"

"I wish!" I spluttered.

For some reason, being able to crack bad-taste jokes made me feel slightly better. We watched Jade kicking up gravel as she stomped on and off gravestones, complaining loudly to herself.

"She's cute," commented Brice.

"I'm amazed you can tell!"

Jade's woolly hat was pulled down so far you could just about see her little nose! Mum had put my little sister in so many layers, she looked like a tiny Arctic explorer.

"Jade, stop that, you're scuffing those new boots," Mum said crossly.

"I don't *like* this ol' cemetery," my sister complained. "Why do we always have to come? Melanie's not even here anyway!"

"Smart as well as cute," Brice said in my ear.

A young cat was picking its way daintily between urns and headstones, clearly heading in our direction. Cats just adore angels.

This one looked like a miniature panther, with his glossy black fur and huge, tawny-gold eyes. He started weaving ecstatically between us, purring so loudly he sounded like a dial tone.

"Mum, Mum, there's a kitty!"

Jade came charging up, scattering gravel.

The cat looked understandably panicky, but Brice crouched down and whispered something in the special language we use for animals, and he instantly relaxed, allowing my sister to pet him.

Jade started confiding secrets to her kitty friend. "My sister's not under that stupid stone you know," she explained in a hoarse whisper. "She goes to a big school in the clouds and she fights all the baddies and monsters with her angel kung fu."

"She's got that *almost* right!" Brice said in my ear.

"My mum says angels don't fight," Jade told the cat, "but I've seed her in my dreams."

I felt slightly dizzy. Had I been sharing Jade's dreams or had she been sharing mine?

Sometimes in nightmares you just think of something scary and it appears.

Under her woolly hat, Jade's brown eyes looked worried. "Oh, no, what's happening to your poor tail?"

Wild-eyed with terror, the cat had fluffed itself out to almost twice its normal size. Ears flat to its skull, it fled, yowling, into the bushes.

I spun to see what had freaked it and almost screamed with shock as I saw the bald shambling beast stumbling towards Jade.

It was a hellhound!

My first thought was that the engraver had got it wrong. Apart from its sick-white skin, which made it look like it was already dead, the hellhound was almost ordinary. It was even behaving like an average family mutt, snuffling along paths and rooting intensely in dark corners. Then, as we watched, the hound lifted its huge naked head, letting out a gargling howl that made every tiny hair stand up on my neck. For a bizarre instant I saw three hounds, all somehow occupying the same space.

I didn't have a second thought.

Brice and I didn't say a word. We instantly sprang between my little sister and the huge hell beast, taking up defensive martial-arts crouches.

I'm not sure if Jade totally realised we were there, but she'd definitely clocked the hellhound. She seemed more fascinated than scared. "Oh, *wow*," she breathed. "That's a really *ugly* monster."

"Don't suppose Sam gave you any flares?" Brice muttered out of the side of his mouth.

I tore open my bag and pulled out two flares, tossing one to Brice.

He quickly bit off the end and was instantly brandishing a huge pillar of golden-white angel fire. I hastily lit mine the same way.

You'd think two torch-wielding angels would have grabbed its attention, but the hellhound was busy snuffling obsessively round my tombstone.

Like the majority of hell creatures, this hound wasn't a real animal; it was a PODS remix of a dog, basically, a collection of evil thoughts trapped inside a nightmare.

I have to say, waiting for a hell beast to notice your existence is v. v. stressful.

"Why doesn't it *see* us," I said in frustration.

"Can't," Brice explained grimly. "Hellhounds are practically blind." He yelled out, "Yo, Fido! Over here!"

"Are you crazy!" I shrieked.

"Trust me," he insisted. "This is the best way!"

Don't ever tell me the worst way then, I thought.

The almost-blind hell beast suspiciously lowered its head, and slowly swivelled in our direction. It had huge, lonely, pain-filled eyes. Who knows what the hellhound saw? Maybe it could just make out a gold-white blur of angel fire? But that seemed like enough.

The hellhound gave a growl so low and menacing that another three hounds seemed to be speaking through its throat. Slippery threads of drool began to drip from its muzzle.

Brice moved so fast, he was like a blur. One minute he was beside me, the next he was standing on a half-toppled tombstone, inches from the hell dog. With one ruthless lunge he shoved the blazing torch into its face.

The hound cringed away, more in loathing than fear, baring hideous outsized canines, and snarling with fury.

"Gotta message for you, hell-pooch!" Brice told it in a chummy voice. "You come near that little girl and I'll insert TWO of these exactly where the sun don't shine."

Incredibly it seemed like Brice had scared it off. The hellhound began to back away, making a frustrated, high-pitched whine, that set my teeth buzzing. It backed so far that it was literally backing *through* a pristine new marble headstone.

Jade immediately ran to my mum. "Mum, mum! There was a monster but Mel and a big boy scared it away with their angel kung fu."

I felt sick just knowing that something so evil could simply erupt into her innocent little world.

Brice sat down on a tombstone, looking shattered.

I watched my parents walk away, very slowly, arm in arm, like they were helping to hold each other up. Jade was skipping beside them, chatting excitedly about monsters.

How I longed to be able to cross back through that invisible barrier and go back to my human world of Sunday parks and Friday night cafés. Unfortunately I'd got trapped in the same world as Brice.

"Thanks," I said with difficulty. "That was great what you just did."

"Nah, just insurance," he said dismissively. "It was never going to hurt Jade."

I didn't need my life to be any more confusing than it already was, so I just snapped at him. "It was never going to hurt her? Oh, really? Wow, so suddenly you talk hell dog now?"

"No. I just happen to know who it's actually following." Brice stood up wearily and just pointed across rows of identical modern headstones, to the wall that divided the cemetery from a three-lane highway outside. He sounded unbelievably depressed.

"See that kid? A while back, he won a hellhound for life."

I was barely in time to see a youth in a hooded top vault over the wall. He plodded beside the traffic until he reached a subway entrance, then disappeared from view.

My mission had taken a bizarre cosmic twist.

Chapter Fifteen

Brice had gone back to his tombstone. I sat down beside him, feeling absolutely unreal.

"That thing is seriously after that boy?" I asked bewildered.

"It's a hound, darling. Give a hound a whiffy trail to follow and off it goes. Only with hellhounds it's not smells, it's vibes."

"That dog was sniffing for *vibes*?"

"If your soul is giving off a certain damaged kind of vibe, the dogs can't help themselves – they'll follow you around till they're half dead sometimes."

Just occasionally, Brice let something drop that made you wonder about all the other darker things which he could never tell anyone, even Lola.

I remembered the beast slobbering obsessively along paths, how frustrated it had seemed when two fire-wielding angels interrupted its icky activities.

I saw Brice had gone off into his own gloomy thoughts.

"So are you planning to keep me in suspense for ever, angel boy, or could you maybe tell me who that hell pooch is really after?"

His face brightened. "Want to meet him? I mean, don't feel you have to, but you can if you really want." He grabbed my wrist to check my watch. "Actually, if we wait just a few minutes then beam ourselves there, I can almost guarantee where he'll be."

I gave a deep sigh. "So where do damaged souls go at ten past three on Sunday afternoons?"

Brice gave me a tired grin. "The Cosmic Café. If business is slow."

When we eventually beamed on to the pavement outside the café, business was about as slow as it could be.

There were exactly two customers, sitting with their backs to each other – an old guy reading a paper and a boy in a hooded top, sitting with his back kind of hunched to the window. Nikos came through the swing doors and carefully set down a plate of steaming sausages and mash in front of the boy.

"See how he's looking after that kid?" I told Brice. "He treats everyone like that."

"Even more amazing when you know Shay's getting a free lunch," Brice commented.

As if he'd heard his name, the boy whipped round. I was startled to see a familiar face with slanting, suspicious brows.

I started to say, "But that's Jordie!"

But suddenly I couldn't breathe.

I *knew* this boy, not from this morning – from *for ever.*

He'd turned back to his meal. I couldn't believe he wasn't as shaken up as I was.

"I'm guessing Shay is Jordie's twin?" I said in a slightly trembly voice. I was trying not to sound anything like as weird as I felt.

Brice was watching me closely. "Didn't you guys ever meet? You seemed like you knew him?"

I shook my head. Kelsey's brothers had never made it to school that often, plus they'd been in a different class. I just had a vague impression of two sets of black slanty eyebrows.

"I sort of knew their older brother."

I started telling Brice how Kelsey and his younger brothers had camped in an abandoned car rather than be taken into care, but he said carelessly, "Yeah, I read about that in the case notes."

I did an amazed double take. "The Agency *assigned* Shay to you! You might have told me you were on a mission, you big creep!"

Ho ho, things were finally adding up! I'd been privately wondering why Brice, of all people, had rocked up in Park Hall, but I could see that a screwed-up boy with a hellhound problem would be just up his street.

Brice shook his head, looking glum. "It's more that Shay assigned himself, if you get my meaning?"

I finally caught on. "Omigosh – you got the call!"

'The call' is when a troubled human sends a personal request for you to be their guardian angel: a silent, totally desperate SOS from their soul to yours. It's a v. mystical event, also a v. v. steep learning curve for the angel who is being called. Now I understood why my friend's boyfriend had seemed so super-stressed.

Brice jammed his hands in his pockets, striking what me and Lola call his 'lonely cosmic outlaw' pose. "To be honest, I'm feeling like I'm in way over my head," he said in a tight voice.

I nodded sympathetically. "I bet. Still it's early days yet, right?"

I was secretly dying to ask him all kinds of nosy questions. Like, could you get rid of a persistent hellhound once it became attached to your vibes, or did it have to follow you around until one of you eventually crumbled into dust? And how did Jordie's brother's soul *become* damaged in the first place?

Lola and I would have been up discussing Shay all night. But it seemed like Brice had said all he wanted to say.

Tell the truth, Mel. I actually got a really strong feeling Brice *wanted* to talk to me about his case, but it was like something was making him hold back.

I thought maybe if I showed a general interest, Brice might feel like he could open up? "So what's Jordie's brother like, anyway?" I asked in a casual voice. "Does he rap too?"

Brice glanced at the boy silently shovelling down everything Nikos had put in front of him.

"I've never even heard that boy talk," he said softly.

Chapter Sixteen

A police helicopter was hovering over the hospital, churning up the night with its blades. After emergency sirens and that constant, pavement-shaking bass line, this sound is the third most common ingredient in Park Hall's edgy urban soundtrack.

Jools and I barely even glanced up as we came out into the freezing wind and rain. After the stuffy atmosphere of the children's ward, the subzero temperatures were a shock.

"That little cutie just *lurves* angel kisses, doesn't he!" Jools enthused through chattering teeth. "Did you see that smile?"

"Yeah, and that clueless nurse said it was wind!"

Four days had gone by since the hellhound incident and my new life as an honorary EA was turning out to be seriously hectic. Up early for dawn vibes, (I know!), plus twice daily rehearsals, and obviously I tried to help out the EAs as much as I could.

After tonight's rehearsal Jools and I had popped in to check on her shocked newborn: the baby who was having problems adjusting to his home planet. I waited, shivering, while Jools checked her phone for messages, then remembered I hadn't actually checked mine for ages.

Most of my messages were from a deeply jealous Lola!

"You guys actually rescued your sister from a *real* live hellhound! AND you're giving angel lessons! Well, take it easy, OK? We don't want any humans sprouting wings, do we? Oh, yeah, tell that creep Brice he has to call me. Miss you!" BEEP

Jools was talking on her phone now, so I ducked into the wheelchair bay out of the wind and rang Lola. Her phone was switched off, *again*, so I left yet another long message, keeping her up to speed with events in Park Hall.

"They're calling the show PURE VIBES, isn't that cool! This production's even got Mrs Threlfall buzzing and trust me, she is not a naturally buzzy lady! She's so thrilled the kids are doing something positive, she's letting them off lessons so they can rehearse! Oh, yeah, remember Miss Rowntree? The teacher who called me an 'airhead with attitude'? She totally can't do enough to help! I know! And obviously it's early days, but working on the show seems to be bringing Karms and Jax even closer."

I felt a pang, because I didn't have anything good to say about Sky.

"Lollie, listen," I remembered. "Brice is having a super-stressful time with his guardian angel module. Send good vibes, yeah?"

When I rang off, I was v. spooked to find a new message from the bad boy himself.

"Got some news that's going to blow you away, but I can't tell you, because you won't get off the stupid *phone*!! Oh, yeah, I'm at KISMET, that little Turkish cafe next to the tattoo parlour!" BEEP.

When Jools and I finally rocked up at KISMET, crackly Arabic music was playing on an ancient cassette player. Brice was watching a group of taxi drivers play dominoes: a game which involved violent slamming on tables, a barrage of friendly insults in at least six different languages, and howls of laughter.

We joined him at his table. "And you're here in this atmospheric cafe because?" Jools hinted.

Brice reluctantly tore himself away. "Oh, yeah, they needed a washer-up." He saw our expressions and rolled his eyes. "Not *me*. Shay's got a few hours work."

"You're waiting to walk him back," I said astonished.

"Just common sense," he said gruffly. "If our four-legged fiend knows Shay's got angelic security, he'll keep his distance, plus it gives us a chance to talk, man-to-man, or cosmic-misfit-to-lost-boy or whatever."

This guardian angel module was bringing out a side to Brice I'd never seen.

"Brice, not to be hardhearted, but what can it actually *do* to him? Obviously being followed by a hellhound isn't ideal, but it's just a nightmare pretending to be a dog, right?"

"Do you guys want to know about this – it's kind of disturbing?"

Brice glanced uneasily at Jools.

"No, I do," I insisted.

He took a breath. "Ok, to put it crudely, a hellhound will only adopt you if you're already in extremely deep poo."

"I can see that."

"Sorry to contradict you, darling, but I don't think you can. I'm talking the *deepest* excrement. Like, say you hurt somebody so badly you can't ever put it right."

Jools suddenly got extra busy arranging her scarf.

I swallowed. "Like you actually *killed* someone?"

"Just for instance," Brice said hastily. "You didn't mean to do it, but – bosh! – it's done."

He pulled a bottle of water out of his pocket and had a long gulp. "You're so horrified and disgusted at yourself, it's not long before those dark voices start up in your head telling you that you're just a bad seed and you shouldn't even be allowed to live. Trouble is, you're freaking scared of dying. That's when hellhounds start sniffing round your Nikes, sweetheart."

"Brice, sorry to sound like a stuck CD, but what can they actually *do* to you?"

"Nothing – and everything. When a hellhound comes into your space, it's like you've got your own hotline into the Hell dimensions. How bad you felt before is nothing to how you feel now. Your vibes drop. You start attracting bad luck. Soon other humans just have to look at you and they *know* you're bad news..."

I had a flash of Shay's face at the café window. Was that what I'd seen? A haunted soul too ashamed to live and too scared to die?

"I can't come to any more rehearsals, Mel," Brice blurted suddenly. "Last night I just went out for like, half-an-hour, just for a break, and when I got back to his kids' home there were tracks right up the hall, and I found more under his bed."

"Under his *bed*!" Jools looked incredibly distressed.

I felt a sorrowful ache deep inside. After all those boys went through, Kelsey's little bro had still ended up in care.

"I just can't see it ending," Brice said in despair. "I know how it's *supposed* to work – that kid *has* to forgive himself, or he'll spend the rest of his life trapped in his own personal hell. I just can't see how it's going to happen, unless—"

Jools swiftly put her hand over his. It was perfectly friendly, but I saw him check himself.

He tried to laugh. "Quite right, Jools. Been watching too much Dr Phil with Shay. Believe it or not I didn't call you to whinge." Brice yanked his phone out of a back pocket and fiddled with some buttons.

"Hold up. Got to find the right picture first. OK, if we just zoom in, it should – *yes*!" He handed me his phone. "That *is* Sky Nolan, right?"

I felt my whole Universe wobble. "Where did you take this?"

"In this café, about an hour ago."

"Here? In *this* cafe?"

You could see him loving my surprise. "Want to see who she was with?"

"Don't keep her in suspense, you pig!"

"OK, see where it says ZOOM OUT? Click on that."

I zoomed and clicked. "Omigosh," I breathed.

There they were, all three Shocking Pinks, drinking Pepsi at the same table, in a Turkish taxi drivers' cafe!

"I couldn't eavesdrop *too* much," he said apologetically. "What with the domino dons over there. But they seemed pretty friendly."

I gazed at the three smiling faces.

This is exactly what our teachers are always banging on about; you give humans the tools and they sort their problems out beautifully all by themselves.

"That was such a lovely thing to do, Brice," I told him tearfully. "Especially when you've got so much else on your plate."

"Don't cry yet," Brice teased. "You haven't even heard the best bit, yet! They've persuaded Sky to be in the show."

"That is SO cool," I gasped. "She's going to do stand-up, right?"

"That was mentioned but she wasn't interested. She wants to introduce the other acts, she says."

I was childishly disappointed, when I should have just been relieved Sky was coming back to school. The past few days she'd totally dropped off my radar. Every time I called in, I'd find her mum and Dan with the boys playing happy families, but no Sky.

Jools pulled a face. "Gotta do my baby-sitting, guys, I'm afraid."

"Want company?" I asked.

She grinned. "We'd just end up talking."

"True," I giggled.

EAs did sometimes keep each other company during the tedious hours of watching absolutely nothing happen on the CCTV monitors. This wasn't the first time I'd offered either. If I had a suspicious nature I'd have thought she just didn't want me around.

I felt like I needed to go back and crash, but instead I sort of hovered. Thanks to Brice I'd had a magic glimpse of the Pinks' reunion, which made me feel even worse about not helping with Shay. Before I could put my guilty feelings into words he pointed sternly at the door.

"Get some rest, angel girl. Got your big show coming off next week, then all that hell trash will go back where it belongs."

My heart suddenly lifted. If the Shocking Pinks were back as a team, the PODS didn't stand a chance!

Chapter Seventeen

The bored red devils on the stage were turning v-e-r-y slowly into unbelievably bored green aliens.

In the wings Tariq was flicking buttons and levers on the school's fancy new computer, making adjustments to his lighting FX.

One alien stumped down off the stage and became a huffy kid again. "I'm off for a smoke," he growled.

For the third time that morning, Tariq whizzed out in his wheelchair to protest. "These guys are jokers, Jax! How can I do my work if they're disrespecting me like this?"

"Stay on your marks, Vibe Tribe," Jax called in a warning voice.

"I would not waste my *energy* disrespecting you, wheelchair boy!" the kid flung at Tariq. "We never even noticed you before you decided to *wheel* yourself right into our special show. I mean what *are* you, man? Just the freaking techie!"

Karmen quickly took him aside. "I know it's boring, Marlon, but Tariq has to know where everyone's going to be on the night, or this show's going to be pure garbage."

"Going to be?!" snorted Jordie, who was going down with a cold.

Jax signalled urgently from across the hall. "Just got a text from Magic Boy. He reckons he's got to drop out – says he's 'hurt his wrist'."

Karmen just crooked her fingers, miming a phone."Call the slacker up, girl! Tell him now he *really* has to do magic!"

"You tell Magic Boy if he don't show up, he gonna answer to the Vibe Tribe," Marlon yelled.

I decided to go for a nice calming walk.

I'd like to tell you that the greatly-improved light levels had turned my depressing school foyer into a wondrous haven of tropical plants, with vibey little fishes speeding about in a shiny new tank. There were some groovy posters which Tariq had designed on his laptop, but as soon as fresh posters went up, other kids instantly defaced them with stupid comments. The truth is, my old school still had all its old hassles and as dark vibes from the hell school gradually percolated though into human reality, new and more disturbing problems started to surface.

Just yesterday, I'd heard Miss Rowntree tell Mr Lupton that kids in her class had worse concentration spans than usual. She put it down to the mystery headaches everyone was getting. Mr Lupton had heard rumours our school might be suffering from 'sick building syndrome'. The EAs and I were like, "Hello!"

Yet despite the odd tantrum and sprained wrist, the cast of PURE VIBES seemed serenely immune to toxic fallout from the PODS school. It was like they were on their own glowy little island.

Jools reckons that if you're one-hundred-per-cent focused on creating something uplifting, it's next-to-impossible for bad vibes to bring you down; and we were seeing daily evidence of the super-positive effects the show was having on kids taking part.

Even Mrs Threlfall had complimented Mr Lupton on the unusually mature and co-operative behaviour of the pupils in the show. We'd been noticing this for a while; in fact Hendrix joked that if we didn't know better, we'd think these kids were turning into angels. Smoking, swearing angels for sure, but that magic spark which Jools was always on about was now actually visible in their eyes.

The feel-good vibes from the show weren't only confined to the cast. One or two were beaming out beyond the school and into the local community. A local hardware store volunteered to donate paint and materials for the atmospheric urban backdrop Karms and Jordie had designed. And you should have seen Tariq's face when his mum rocked up with ladies from her Women Aglow keep-fit club, bringing Tupperware boxes crammed with little goodies which they'd baked especially for the cast! He looked ready to die of shame!

I felt a sudden rush of relief. Sky had just walked into the foyer. Two hours late, but as she told the others, "All I do is be cute and read cue cards. How much rehearsal does that actually take!"

The first time my mate had rehearsed her links, I was worried she couldn't hack it. She drifted out on to the stage, looking totally out of it – until they switched on the mike. Then, after a slightly shaky start, the old sassy, flirty Sky kicked back in like she'd never been away. In that moment it was like she was born to be a link girl. She had this hilarious way of bigging up the performers' acts which was totally OTT, yet it worked.

Karmen and Jax said the audience was going to love her.

The rest of the cast didn't seem so sure. "I get a bad vibe off that girl," Jordie told Marlon. "She think I don't notice but deep down she laughing at us, man."

It upset me to hear that, partly because I knew what he meant. Sky had a faintly patronising way of treating the other cast members, like they were endearing little five year olds putting on a puppet show for their mummies and daddies behind the sofa.

I wasn't comfortable with this new superior Sky. I was also deeply disappointed by her casual attitude to the other Pinks. When she'd originally agreed to be in their show, I'd pictured them hanging out together almost constantly, like before. In fact she hardly saw Jax and Karmen outside rehearsals.

But like I tried to tell Helix, it's an ancient cosmic law; when girls get boyfriends, everything else goes out the window.

My inner angel had been out of touch for a while and I was starting to miss her. I'd sent a few hopeful probes into mystical inner space suggesting it would be nice to catch up, but all I got was one of those TV info streams flashing across my mind going: *SHAY SHAY SHAY SHAY SHAY.*

I just beamed a stroppy message right back: *Thanks for nothing, girl! Like I don't feel guilty enough. Mind telling me how I'm supposed to help Brice with Shay AND work on a show, AND make sure my friends don't backslide?*

Immediately after that night's rehearsal, Jools had to beam back to Matilda Street to dash off an assignment for a course she was taking in Dark Studies. I needed a walk after the total madness of the show, so I walked back alone.

I hadn't been past the Cosmic Café for days, so I was shocked to see someone had sprayed graffiti on the door. Maybe Nikos had started cleaning it off. Now it just said: SHAY IS A MUR...

You're gonna get yours Shay. We know what you did Shay.

It was like someone had shaken a kaleidoscope; suddenly I was seeing a new disturbing pattern. Like I told you, spraying graffiti is a well-known leisure activity in my neighbourhood, and Shay is such a common local name that my brain hadn't made a connection with the other hate graffiti I'd seen when I arrived. Now it seemed like the same ill-wisher had been out to get Brice's Shay all the time.

The café must have been having a slow night, because Shay was inside, polishing his plate with his last piece of bread. Brice kept a careful watch from a nearby table, clearly in need of some space.

I wondered why his hell-dog boy preferred to eat free meals in the café instead of eating at the kids' home; but mostly I wondered how he could still swallow, with those malicious words splattered on the door for the world to see.

I saw Shay getting up to leave. Worried that Brice might think I was checking up on him, I stepped back into the shadows as they came out of the door. Brice was chatting to Shay now in a bravely upbeat voice. As I watched Shay trudge away, unaware of his loyal bodyguard, I felt like I had never seen such a broken-looking kid.

There were now just two nights to go before the final show. The EAs had planned a super-thorough cosmic sweep down at the school. Jools called Brice up and offered to mind Shay while he went down to the school with that night's 'sweepers'.

"He said I saved his life," she grinned when she rang off. "The kids at the home were watching When Good Pets Turn Bad!"

I don't know if this was Brice's idea, but for the first time the EAs invited me to go along on the sweep. When we reached the school, we had to split into pairs. Each pair was responsible for sweeping a different area of the school. Brice and I got the annexe, the area where the crack between the dimensions first appeared.

Since the afternoon of the evil hell turd, I hadn't risked setting foot on that bridge, let alone crossing it, so I'd never seen the actual site of the leak. I suspect that's why I'd been invited along. Brice thought it was time I knew the score.

One thing's for sure; terms like 'crack' and 'leak' don't come near describing the hideously hyperactive evil portal in the boys' changing rooms.

I backed in revulsion from the swirling sucking thing in the floor, then got a double jolt of horror as I saw the ghostly green graffiti on the changing room wall, the words still visible through the watered-down emulsion. YOU WON'T GET AWAY WITH IT SHAY.

The graffiti was quite old, yet the hate vibes coming at me from the wall still packed enough of a cosmic punch to make me feel physically shaky. I heard myself blurt out, "Did the EAs ever find out how that crack started?"

Brice's tone was deliberately super-casual. "Not really. They've got a few theories. We know when it appeared though," he added, like he just thought he'd mention it. "By a weird coincidence it was exactly the same time as your funeral."

Chapter Eighteen

Mr Allbright once gave out this cute little print-out explaining why the Universe is exactly like your ideal soul-mate.

One example I remember is that when the Universe sends you helpful signs, and you totally refuse to pay attention, instead of going into a major huff and washing its hands of you, it generously sends bigger, even more disturbing, signs, until weeks, or maybe it's centuries, later, you finally get the message.

I'm only telling you this because I was just about to get a deeply disturbing sign.

It was the evening of the dress rehearsal and the night before the show. The rehearsal went brilliantly. Jordie was over his cold, Magic Boy had recovered from his mysterious 'injury', and Marlon stood on his mark like a pro.

Unfortunately it was Jools' night to baby-sit the Powers of Darkness, which was a shame, because for the first time the kids were performing to a select audience. At least ten other teachers joined Mr Lupton and Miss Rowntree in the hall for a preview of PURE VIBES.

Afterwards they seemed genuinely impressed, though I did see two female teachers tutting over Sky's tiny clingy dress.

Sky seemed as delighted as everyone else that things had gone so well. I actually saw her throw her arms round Karmen and give her a genuinely affectionate hug.

Karmen's eyes narrowed suddenly. "What's this in your hair, girl?" She tried to pick off the teeny acid-green splodge.

Sky winced away, half laughing. "Ow, don't! It's paint, you muppet! I've been helping my brothers decorate their room and of course Olly has to start a paint fight! Now their bunk beds look exactly like modern art!"

I felt as if all the breath had been knocked out of me. That's because I knew something Karms and Jax couldn't possibly know.

It was a cute family picture Sky was painting, but the only time she went back to her mum's these days was to blag money off Dan, and maybe grab a change of clothes.

And for the record, the green paint in her hair was not the kind you use in a little kid's room. It was the kind you get in a spray can. The kind bored or angry kids use to spray graffiti.

I just beamed myself straight to the Nolans' flat.

I was literally frantic, pushing my head into closed drawers and cupboards, almost sobbing, "Don't let it be here, please please please don't let it be here." I was abusing the cosmic angels' gift to invade my friend's privacy and it felt like the *most* shameful thing ever.

When I finally found the aerosol cans, wrapped in her paint-stained hoody, I still couldn't take it in. I found myself making excuses for her; she'd had a disturbed childhood, the graffiti at the Cosmic Café was just a stupid one-off, any number of kids could have splattered those other hate-filled words around Park Hall.

But I knew it had always been Sky.

I beamed back to Matilda Street and pounded up flights of stairs to the room where Jools was baby-sitting the PODS.

This door was always kept shut now, but I rushed in without even knocking. "Jools!" I gasped. "Something awful's—"

Jools practically dived to block my view of the monitors, in a belated attempt to stop me seeing the devastating sight.

I couldn't move.

There she was on camera, just letting herself through the shabby back door. I glimpsed shadowy stairs and a floor littered with junk mail, then the door closed.

"She had a key?" I whispered. "She had a key to *that* house?"

Night after night, Sky had waved laughing goodbyes to the other Pinks and gone straight to this evil place.

Jools was in tears. "I'm so sorry, Mel."

"Were you ever going to tell me?" I asked numbly.

"It just never felt like the right *time*," she almost wailed. "You were doing so well with the others, we started to think maybe you could help Sky too. When she agreed to be in the show, we all thought that was *such* a hopeful sign. I *still* think that production could turn her around."

"She doesn't care zip about the show," I said in a bleak voice. "Jordie's right not to trust her. It's Sky who's writing that hate graffiti about Shay – that's what I came to tell you."

Jools looked genuinely shocked. "How do you know?"

"Karms found paint in her hair. I checked Sky's room and found, well, evidence." I let out a choking little sob. "It's almost funny – on my way back here I thought things were about as bad as they could be. But they were so *so* much worse!"

Jools was practically wringing her hands. "She's not a bad person, Mel, you have to believe that. That girl is just so totally *desperate* to belong to someone."

I sat down and covered my face. "Let's face it – you've got to be a bit desperate to date a PODS," I said with a slightly hysterical laugh.

"No, I *swear*," Jools said in a pleading voice. "We checked that out. He's just an unsavoury human boy sharing a really unsavoury squat."

"Unsavoury! Hello!!" I said from behind my hands.

I wasn't mad at the earth angels. I was mad at myself.

The Universe had sent enough signs. The instant I heard that ringtone, I knew. *Something bad HAS happened to her*, Helix had said.

Without me to keep her on track, Sky had taken a wrong *wrong* turning. Now she couldn't turn back; she had way too much hate and pain stored up in her heart. Did she even *know* why she hated Shay so much, or did she just need someone to hate? I couldn't begin to guess the answers.

I just knew one thing. Tomorrow, a troubled girl with an evil boyfriend was presenting a show in a school with a dangerous cosmic leak; and there wasn't a thing we could do to stop her.

Chapter Nineteen

Jax and Karms had insisted all performers should be backstage one hour at least before the world premiere of PURE VIBES kicked off.

They all made it, even Magic Boy. One of the girls from an R&B group called the Hussies had to be sick in the toilets, but she was there.

The first act was unannounced. Twenty kids in dazzling white judo suits just exploded on to the stage and did an electrifying display of a Brazilian martial arts form called *Kapoeira*, the closest thing I've seen to angelic fighting styles.

The kids ran off to astonished applause and Sky flew on to introduce the second act. In the wings, for just an instant, she'd gone deathly white, but now she was at the mike for real, you wouldn't think she had a nerve in her body. She was actually better than in rehearsals – maybe because the audience so obviously loved her – and she was getting all those warm vibes streaming back.

Sky used to say the thing in comedy is timing. When we screamed with laughter at one of her fave female comics, she'd tell us, "It's all about timing, guys. OK, it's partly how she says it, but that's not nearly so important as when."

Possibly it's the same with revenge.

Sky waited so long for the moment she and the boyfriend had planned, I started to think Jools had got it right. Like the other Pinks, Sky had finally, and miraculously, turned a corner.

You know what? I think that almost happened.

All that warm human approval coming back from the audience did start to penetrate some frozen place in Sky that angel vibes couldn't reach; showing my friend not just what she could be, but who she really was.

When she ran on to introduce the Hussies, she looked so lovely and luminous that I almost dared to hope.

Jordie's was the last act but one. The idea was to hand the audience over to the Vibe Tribe totally buzzing, so they could lift the roof with a final feel-good set which they'd dedicated v. touchingly to my memory.

Before Sky could go out to introduce him, Jordie just barged past her on to the stage. "I don't need no freaking introduction, man," he growled over his shoulder. "I'm gonna just storm on and slay all the people dead with my charisma!"

Jordie's rap was called Pressure, and it was about the pressures of growing up in Park Hall. As he prowled around the stage, spitting lyrics, you could see parents becoming visibly moved. Through this furious, rapping boy, they could almost feel how hard it was for their kids.

After long talks with Karmen, the rap had recently acquired an almost hopeful ending. The Hussies slipped back on stage, becoming Jordie's backing singers as he rapped more softly:

"Used to be some forests when this world was new.

Then evolution carbonise 'em. Same with me and you.

Pressure keep a coming, squeezin' diamonds outa coal.

Same thing happenin' to us kids in Park Hall."

The audience went crazy. People stomped and shouted. Jordie stormed off stage the way he came on, but he was almost crying now.

I was in the wings when Sky went on to introduce the final act. She took the mike from the stand and waited until the audience calmed down.

"Well, guys, it's almost the end of our show, and the Vibe Tribe are waiting in the wings to play their special tribute for Mel."

Sky's voice always took on a special serious tone for her final link. "Everyone who knew Mel knows how she would have been loving this show. Sadly she can't be with us. Just a few hours after her thirteen birthday, she was tragically killed. But we've all felt her with us while we were rehearsing and she's particularly in our thoughts today."

Sky deliberately threw down her cue cards.

"I know Jordan Hickman must be thinking about Mel a lot," she said in a conversational voice.

Karms and Jax exchanged alarmed glances. This wasn't in the script.

"I always wonder how he can get those lyrics out," Sky said in the same chatty tone. "They must break him up. That bit about '*trying to run faster than the murder machine, and he can't find the brake pedal and the wheels keep turning'*. That's so exactly how that joyrider must have felt when he murdered Mel."

A chilling new vibe was creeping into the hall. People in the audience looked uncomfortable as Sky babbled on about Jordie's lyrics.

"Get her off, Jordie," Jax hissed. "Do another rap if you have to."

When Sky saw Jordie coming out of the wings, she gave a theatrical gasp. "Jordie, I'm SO sorry!! I just realised you probably didn't even know?" Sky looked down at her fingernails. There was an electric silence in the hall. She had everyone mesmerised with her bizarre behaviour. When she finally looked up again, there was a weird little smile playing at the corners of her mouth.

"You probably had no idea who was driving that stolen car?"

She deliberately met Jordie's eyes.

"You genuinely didn't know it was your brother who killed my best friend," she asked in a breathy insincere voice.

There was a collective gasp.

"Poor Jordie," Sky sighed. "What a truly terrible

way for you to find out – in front of all these people!"

And not only for Jordie.

My knees had totally gone from under me. I was hearing screaming brakes and smelling burning rubber. I saw raw rusty metal and a white terrified face: the last face I'd seen in this world.

Now that face finally had a name.

"You'll get yours, Shay!"

Jordie just walked off stage and would have kept walking right out of the building if Jax and Karms hadn't forcibly grabbed on to him.

Marlon and the rest of the Vibe Tribe had been waiting to go on. Now they looked paralysed with shock.

How had she known? And if she knew, why didn't she just *tell* someone, instead of exposing Shay and his brothers in public like this?

Obviously just putting him in prison wasn't enough to satisfy her thirst for revenge at losing her friend. Shay's brothers, and the entire community, had to be punished too.

Well, Sky had punished Park Hall big time. You could see people's faces closing up like clams. I heard booing, and someone angrily kicked over a chair as they walked out. You could feel the vibes dropping, first to levels more normal for Bell Meadow, and then they kept on dropping.

When you raise expectations in a place like Park Hall, then cruelly dash them, the shock to human souls makes them feel like there's no hope anywhere and their world has become a howling void.

Killing hope is what the PODS do best.

Next comes getting others to do their dirty work. Sky's petty act of human revenge was nothing to what the Dark Powers had planned.

My heart turned over as I saw that other darker school starting to show clearly now through the walls. Now it was the human school which felt unreal, as the hell vortex in the changing rooms opened to the max, releasing hideous howls and whisperings and a rush of clammy stinking wind which you could smell in the school hall.

Desperate for comfort, I was unconsciously fiddling with Reuben's charm bracelet, going *this charm is for protection, this charm is for protection...*

Jools clutched at my hand. This was our fault. We'd added too much light to Park Hall's darkness, treating these troubled kids like angels in waiting. *Don't want any humans growing wings*, Lola had joked. We'd raised them up so high, but we'd never got round to teaching them how to fly.

The darkness in the hall visibly curdled and thickened, as the first hell trash came skittering and slithering in from the foyer. Hell trash is the lowest, most fast-breeding cosmic life form; think of normal earth vermin – rats or cockroaches – hideously remixed by the PODS, and you'll get an idea of the sheer vileness of these creatures. They were being sent in to drag the light levels down to an all-time low, so the PODS to complete the school switch.

The human audience couldn't see the hell trash, or hear the hell sounds or the evil whiplash voices of the shadowy teachers herding their dead-eyed pupils over the bridge into the school hall. But they must have felt them, because they were suddenly completely desperate to leave.

But my friends weren't going to let them go without a fight.

Karmen practically ran out of the wings and took the mike. She was shaking with fury. "I can't believe you're walking out on us!" she blazed at the astonished audience. "Did you love our show or not? YES you did! Weren't you freaking gobsmacked that your kids could actually pull this off. YES you were! So you might at least wait to hear what we've got to SAY about it?"

The audience was so surprised to find themselves being told off by a tiny Asian girl with a lisp, that they just took it.

Karms pointed a shaking finger at Sky. "Maybe one day I'll be able to forgive you for disrespecting all the pure love we've all put into this show. But you made a big mistake when you disrespected Melanie. Mel wasn't about this, Sky. How could you call yourself a Shocking Pink and *not* know that?"

Now Jax came pushing up to the mike. "Say what you like about us, Sky. We're still here to defend ourselves, yeah, but you didn't just sabotage our show, you tried to poison that lovely girl's memory and we can't allow that. This show made me feel like I was part of something," she told the audience, choking with emotion. "I never felt like that. I miss Mel, but these have been..." her entire face quivered as she sobbed out the last words "...the two happiest weeks of my life!"

If the audience was stunned, that was nothing to the PODS. The clammy hell winds from the annexe seemed to falter as the light evels inched up a tiny notch.

That's all it took. Under the alarmed clickings and warblings of the hell trash, I heard the electronic hum of a wheelchair as Tariq came punting out of the wings with a v. determined expression. Behind him came a pale, stricken Jordie, quickly followed by the entire Vibe Tribe. Then the Hussies, Magic Boy and twenty kapoeira kids filed on from the wings, all taking their places defiantly beside Jax and Karmen. Even Mr Lupton and Miss Rowntree hurried up out of the audience to declare their support.

Karmen's eyes widened as she looked out into the hall. "They're coming back! Start singing, you muppets!"

The Vibe Tribe bravely launched into "Where is the Love?"

I felt the ends of my hair start to tingle. Strong new voices were joining in my fave Black Eyed Peas song. The light levels began to lift as angels came beaming down everywhere.

Among them I saw familiar faces, earth angels I'd chatted to on Hampstead Heath: the girl who worked with street kids, a boy with a rucksack, a stern business man in a beautiful suit.

All the Matilda Street angels had come – Hendrix and Tallulah, Dino and Delphine – and still new angels kept on arriving, until the hall shone and shimmered with their light.

Jools had said London had seven energy hot spots, but just then it felt like there were eight.

With so many angels crowding into one place, our grungey school hall suddenly seemed like the loveliest place on Earth.

Unless you belong to the Powers of Darkness.

The hell trash clicked and warbled their panic, tumbling over each other in their desperation to escape. The shadowy teachers and pupils were actually morphing in and out of each other as they fled, driven from the hall by the overwhelming light generated by such a massive influx of angels.

Sky had shown no trace of emotion while the kids were furiously defending the honour of their show, but now she looked panicky. She couldn't see the angels or the mass exodus of the PODS, but the madly soaring light levels must have made her feel like she was in the wrong place. Suddenly she bolted from the hall.

"Help me!" I called to Jools, "or she's going to be sucked down that *thing* with the hell trash!"

We went hurtling after Sky.

Caught up in the invisible stampede back to the vortex, she was running crazily towards the bridge.

She never reached it.

I heard a cold voice call her name.

When Sky spun to see the youth standing in the foyer she gave a sob of relief. "Oh, Billy!" She rushed to him.

"They're still singing in there," he said coldly. "What happened?"

"I don't *know*!" she wailed. "I did everything right. I don't understand why it didn't freaking work!" Sky tried to cling on to him, and I saw him angrily shaking her off as they left the building.

I yearned to help my friend get back her self-respect, but I'd finally realised this wasn't my job. Like Jools told me once; sometimes angels think they have to help one kid, when it's a totally different kid who needed you all the time.

When Brice saw Jools and I walk into the Cosmic Café, he looked like he was too afraid to even hope.

"It's OK," I mouthed to him. "I *know*."

It's a bit unreal, meeting your killer in your neighbourhood café, and finally knowing that this was the same human soul who sent you zooming out of human history into a whole new career direction.

The café was steamy with good cooking smells. I could hear Nikos laughing in the kitchen.

For once Shay had hardly touched his meal. He was just staring emptily into space.

Jools and I sat down at his table, gently covering his hands with ours. I felt a deep tremor go through me, as Shay's soul connected with mine, and in one shocking jolt, I saw it all.

Shay high on his joyride, then desperately trying to brake, and eventually crashing into a bollard further on. I watched him stumble off into Bell Meadow, cut and bleeding, so sick with guilt and horror that he could never tell another soul.

This was Shay Hickman's version of our story, and though both our stories were equally true, they were as different as day from night. Shay's version of my death was about shame and endings. Mine shimmered with joyful new beginnings, a magical flight through the Universe, a scholarship to the coolest angel school in the cosmos, a blissful reunion with my soul-mate, and another special friendship with the angel girl who was sitting with me in Nikos' café, softly holding Shay's other hand.

In that moment I felt my heart just fly open. I had everything, but Shay had nothing, and it was down to me now to set this right.

With the hum of the café all around, I hitched my chair closer and started talking.

Most of what I said was for Shay's ears only. I'll just tell you what I told him just before we left. I leaned in and whispered right into his ear. "I totally forgive you, Shay," I told him huskily. "You have a truly beautiful heart, and I'll tell you something else. I know you feel like you're all alone, but that's not true. Angels are watching over you twenty-four-seven, Shay, and if you ever feel able to let us, we'd really like to help you, yeah?"

Sadly Shay Hickman had been so deep-frozen for so long that thawing out could take a long while – plus it was going to hurt big time. That's when he'd really need his faithful guardian angel.

At the door, Jools and I turned back to give Brice an encouraging wave, and were stunned to see Shay taking out his mobile. He was shaking so much that at first he couldn't get the number.

"Kelsey," he said in a choked voice. "It's me. I'm – I'm in some pretty bad trouble, man." He was crying. I was in tears too.

It was only now that I understood what a desperately delicate mission the Agency had entrusted to me and Brice. That angel boy had known all along that I was the one being in the Universe who could release him and Shay from their mutual ordeal; but he couldn't tell me, because for this to be real, I had to choose to forgive Shay, from my deepest core, so he could start to live – perhaps for the very first time.

Outside the café, Jools saw how wobbly I was feeling and instantly hooked her arm through mine.

"So now you've saved your school from the evil hell vortex, angel girl, what do you want to do in your few remaining minutes!"

When the Agency is about to bring agents back home, there's a particular vibe in the air. But I didn't feel ready to say goodbye to my new friend just yet, so we sauntered on, chatting about what we'd do on her next trip to Heaven, as if we had all the time in the world.

Maybe my heart was still wide open from forgiving Shay, because even though this was Park Hall and not Heaven, I could see rainbow sparkles round all the passers-by.

Jools and I finally said emotional goodbyes outside the Buddhist wholefood shop, then I wistfully returned my borrowed Parka, and Jools thoughtfully lent me her rainbow scarf to keep me warm until I got back to Heaven. You see I had one last call to make.

To my surprise the lights were on in the sitting room.

My mum and step-dad were still up, poring over holiday brochures, planning their first ever holiday. I kissed each of them lovingly on the tops of their heads, then I peeped in on Jade.

My little sister was snoring softly, her fingers still gripping a red crayon. She'd fallen asleep in the middle of drawing me a picture. At the top it said:

TO MEl BEEbY, AngLE SKOOl, HEvun.

The drawing showed two little stick figures facing off a huge three-headed monster.

I gave Jade exactly three smacking angel kisses, breathing in her sleepy wax-crayon smell for the last time, then I whispered, "I'll be back soon, Fluffyhead, don't worry, but you're going to be fine now – all the bad monsters are gone. You'll just have sweet dreams from now on, I promise."

Then a whoosh of white light enfolded me, taking me home.

Don't miss the amazing mission that started it all...

winging it

TIME: My 13th Birthday

PLACE: Heaven

MISSION: Enrol at angel school!

REPORT: One minute I'm crossing the road, working out the clothes I'm going to buy with my birthday money, then – BANG! – I'm a student in some posh angel school, learning about halos. At least the uniforms are cool...

www.agentangel.co.uk

Don't miss Mel Beeby's second amazing mission...

losing the plot

TIME: My 16th Birthday

PLACE: London

MISSION: Rescue a teenage trio!

REPORT: A "delicate situation" the boss calls it. Chaos more like! The Powers of Darkness are strong and that creepy agent Brice is in town. We have to act fast...

Don't miss Mel Beeby's third amazing mission...

flying high

TIME: 20th Centruy

PLACE: France

MISSION: Prepare to Party!

REPORT: The call comes at Lola's birthday beach party. The good news? We're off on a Children's Crusade. The bad news? An evil time travel scam, that creep Brice – and I'm still wearing my silk sarong and flip-flops!

Don't miss Mel Beeby's fourth amazing mission...

calling the shots

TIME: 20th Centruy

PLACE: Hollywood

MISSION: Get into showbiz!

REPORT: My first mission as a solo Guardian Angel and I've got serious stage fright! It may look exciting in the movies, but life is dangerous in tinsel town, even for someone as angelic as me...